PELICAN BOOKS
A183
BRITISH HERBS
BY
FLORENCE RANSON

BRITISH HERBS

BY FLORENCE RANSON

*

WITH ILLUSTRATIONS BY
EDITH LONGSTRETH THOMPSON

*

PENGUIN BOOKS

Penguin Books Ltd, Harmondsworth, Middlesex

U.S.A.: Penguin Books Inc., 3300 Clipper Mill Road, Baltimore 11, Md
[*Educational Representative:*
D. C. Heath & Co., 285 Columbus Avenue, Boston 16, Mass]

CANADA: Penguin Books (Canada) Ltd, 47 Green Street,
Saint Lambert, Montreal, P.Q.

AUSTRALIA: Penguin Books Pty Ltd, 762 Whitehorse Road,
Mitcham, Victoria

SOUTH AFRICA: Penguin Books (S.A.) Pty Ltd, 218 Grand Parade Centre,
Adderley Street, Cape Town

—

First published 1949
Reprinted 1954

Made and printed in Great Britain
by Richard Clay and Company, Ltd, Bungay, Suffolk

This book is dedicated to
JEFFERY BOHUN RANSON,
Bomber Command, R.A.F.V.R.,
for whom my Herb Garden was made,
in Remembrance

★

Excellent herbs had our fathers of old,
  Excellent herbs to heal their pain,
Alexanders and Marigold,
  Eyebright, Orris and Elecampane.
Basil, Rocket, Valerian, Rue,
  Almost singing themselves they run.
Vervain, Dittany, Call-me-to-you,
  Cowslip, Melilot, Rose of the sun –
Anything green that grew out of the mould
Was an excellent herb to our fathers of old.

REWARDS AND FAIRIES
by Rudyard Kipling

ACKNOWLEDGMENTS

I WOULD like to acknowledge most gratefully the help I have received from Mr C. Smith (Secretary of the Vegetable Drugs Committee), Dr R. Butcher, B.Sc., Ph.D. (National Herb Organiser), Mr A. R. G. Chamings, B.Pharm., and Mr S. K. Samways (both of the Rose Hips Products Association), and all the many other friends who have helped me with ideas and suggestions. The photographs appear by courtesy of Messrs. Stafford, Allen and Sons, Ltd, of Long Melford, Suffolk.

FLORENCE RANSON

East Hanningfield,
Chelmsford

CONTENTS

*

INTRODUCTION

DURING my six years as County Secretary of the Essex Herb Committee it soon became clear to me that many country people had never had the opportunity of learning about the wonderful wealth of wild flowers that strew our countryside for so many months in the year. And, except for a few enthusiasts here and there, the knowledge of the majority with regard to herbs was usually confined to rather vague ideas about nettle tea and herb beer.

At all the meetings and exhibitions where I took specimens of delicious-scented herb-plants the question arose as to where a simple book with illustrations could be obtained, telling something of the history of herbs and the uses to which they are put.

I hope, therefore, that this little book will not only bring back many happy memories to our thousands of energetic herb-collectors, but also that it will encourage more people to seek out these 'excellent herbs', and, in some cases, devote a part of their cultivated land to that most fragrant and satisfying plot – 'A Garden of Herbs'.

This book is not intended to deal with the botanical aspect of medicinal plants, but to give general information about them. Those wishing to learn something more of the structure and classification of plants can take as their guides Bentham and Hooker's *Handbook of the British Flora*, Johns' *Flowers of the Field* or the able work of Dr. John Hutchinson, *Common Wild Flowers*, published by Penguin Books, or any other of the large range of books on wild flowers to be obtained from booksellers and libraries.

DEFINITION OF HERBS

One cannot help wondering how medicinal herbs came to be selected from those with no healing properties, and it can only be surmised that in those far-off days in the childhood of the world, when man's guiding interest was his never-ending quest

9

for food, every wild plant was tested by the method of trial and error, and those that had some economic or medicinal value have survived either as grain, roots, fruit or herbs. This selecting was a perpetual process, and though science is still sorting out the good from the less useful, knowledge of herbal botany is far from complete.

The word 'herbs' is now used in a limited sense, and has come to mean only those plants that are useful either for medicine or for cookery, but originally it meant any kind of plant – 'herb bearing seed after his kind' – or, as the dictionary says, 'a soft or succulent plant that dies at the root every year' – the idea that is still contained in the word 'herbage'. In early times a medicinal plant was often indicated by the Anglo-Saxon name of 'wort', as in 'Woundwort' or 'St John's Wort'.

HERBS SELECTED

It is not at all an easy matter to select for this book those plants which still have a medicinal value, as herbalists and druggists vary very much in the choice of the plants which they stock. But I have tried to describe the most important herbs, many of them with some specially distinctive scent, which are used in pharmacy, and of which a good number are included in the *British Pharmacopoeia* and the *British Pharmaceutical Codex*. (The *British Pharmacopoeia* is published under the direction of the General Council of Medical Education and Registration of the United Kingdom, and the *British Pharmaceutical Codex* under the auspices of the Pharmaceutical Society of Great Britain.)

I have not included those precious rare plants such as the quaint little Sundew, the gorgeous Pasque Flower (*Anemone pulsatilla*), the green-flowered Hellebores, the dainty Cyclamen and the purple Columbine, sometimes seen in Herb catalogues, for the ruthless extinction of these and other rare plants would be a great loss to the British countryside. Nor do I think it necessary to cover the many wild flowers prescribed in minute doses in homoeopathic medicine, as details of these can be obtained from the literature devoted to this subject.

I have dealt mainly with a small number of British herbs which grow wild, but have, of course, included in one section those many delicious culinary and flavouring herbs which have for hundreds of years been grown in British gardens.

A large number of valuable drug-plants grow outside the British Isles; the United States, with its great divergencies of soil and climate, produces many useful herbs, as well as India, the West Indies, China and South America. In fact, just as medicine is an international science, so are the healing herbs used in pharmacy scattered broadcast throughout the world for the benefit of all its peoples.

Since the fifteenth century, when roving seamen brought home rare and valuable plants, attempts have been made to naturalise them in this country, but though some, such as the potato and tomato, have been able to adapt themselves to our variable soil and climate, a good number are quite unsuitable.

Mention must, however, be made of some of these foreigners, as they play so vital a part in medicine, and some of them can be grown here under special conditions in botanic gardens or green-houses. For instance, until the last few years no drug was so beneficial for the treatment of ague and malaria as quinine, which is derived from the bark of a Peruvian tree, *Cinchona succiruba*. The Spaniards discovered it in Peru about 1639, and it was named after the Countess of Cinchon, wife of the Spanish Viceroy, who was cured of 'a feverish complaint', probably ague or malaria, by the use of the bark. The Countess returned to Spain, taking the bark with her, and it was then called 'Jesuit's Bark', as it was given to the Jesuit fraternity. Gradually its fame spread throughout Europe, and its appearance in England at a time when ague was greatly prevalent, and the fact that Charles II was cured of this disease by its agency, increased its popularity. But the great value of this plant was fully appreciated only when it made possible through the centuries the colonisation by the white peoples of the tropical parts of the world.

'Hearbe Tabaco' was first brought to this country from the West Indies by that famous sailor, Sir John Hawkins (not Sir Walter Raleigh, to whom its introduction is often ascribed). Its leaves were first used to alleviate toothache, and, as Gerard says, 'against paines in the head, stomack, catarrhs and rheums'. Any cure that resulted was probably due to the alkaloid, nico-tine, still largely used in medicine, and, as all gardeners know, as a pest-killer. Tobacco can be grown in the warmer parts of Eng-land, but is not cultivated there commercially, for various economic reasons.

Camphor (*Cinnamomum camphora*) is a native of China and Japan. Everyone is familiar with its beneficial effects, and the lack of it was greatly felt during the six years of war. It will not grow in the English climate, but a herb called the Camphor plant (*Balsamita vulgaris*), which has a strong camphor scent, can be quite easily cultivated. The dried leaves have the same merit of keeping away moths as the genuine Chinese Camphor.

Balsam Tolu (*Myroxylon toluifera*) is one of the important ingredients of many cough and bronchial lozenges, as may be seen by studying the labels on the containers of these tablets. It is not related to the British balsams and balms.

The invaluable Witch Hazel (*Hamamelis virginiana*), used as a styptic, astringent and antiseptic drug both in lotions and ointments, is, as the name indicates, a native of North America, where it abounds. It is often grown in this country for its decorative appearance, but is not cultivated commercially to any extent.

Tincture of squills, derived from the Sicilian Squill (*Urginea scilla*), is useful in chest complaints and heart affections, and many forms of it are recorded in the Pharmacopoeias. This is not the species common in English bulb borders.

The best Quassia comes from Jamaica, and is well known in Britain as a pest-killer and in medicine as a tonic and for alleviating digestive ailments. Golden Seal (*Hydrastis canadensis*) is, with a certain amount of difficulty, grown commercially in Britain, but is a native of Canada and eastern America. It is one of the most valued of drugs, being employed as a tonic, laxative, and for digestive and liver troubles.

Cinnamon, ginger and pepper are known to us mostly as culinary spices, but they are also used in medicine, ginger being one of the flavours used for neutralising unpleasant tastes. Gerard had sadly to admit that Ginger, having 'been broughte unto me at severall times from the West Indies, is most impatient of the coldnesse of these our northerne climes, as myselfe have found by proofe'. As the home of this herb is in tropical districts, this was scarcely to be wondered at.

The Castor-oil plant (*Ricinus communis*), though originally a native of India, has been introduced into sub-tropical districts, and was also successfully cultivated in Italy, the oil being experimented with as an alternative to mineral oils for aircraft. Though not grown here commercially, it is often seen in greenhouses or as an ornamental plant.

Cascara sagrada (Californian Buckthorn), which grows wild

in the United States, belongs to the same genus as the Buckthorn of our English woods, also employed for its purgative properties.

Eucalyptus from Australia, a valuable antiseptic, and also a beautiful addition to many English gardens, must not be forgotten.

So one might continue to enumerate these good 'fruits of the earth', brought to us in normal times in vast prodigality from the far corners of the world.

But if the United States has benefited our country with so many valuable drugs, a considerable contribution has been made in return, as can be seen from the books of 'John Josselyn, Gentleman' of Boston of the seventeenth century. In these he describes with pride the cultivation of 'precious herbs' – Mint, Thyme, Lavender, Sage, Marjoram, Liquorice and others – brought from the 'Old Country' by the early settlers. This Herb Garden was evidently tended with much care, for later on a pharmacy store was started in Boston, and to-day this same town is the headquarters of The Herb Society of America.

HERBS OF THE BIBLE

The question is often asked whether the herbs, such as Mint, Anise and Cumin, mentioned in the Bible are the same as the plants grown in our kitchen gardens. Though the Hebrews obtained most of their 'precious oils' and herb plants from the East along the caravan routes, many flavouring plants – Mint, Thyme, Sage and Marjoram – are natives of Syria and Palestine, and came to us through the Romans.

Though Anemones are not now much used as drugs in Britain, the glorious Poppy Anemone (*Anemone coronaria*), believed to be 'the lily of the field' of the New Testament, gaily adorning our herbacious borders in springtime, is put to medicinal purposes in many countries. Dill and Cumin, to which reference is made, are grown commercially in Britain, though Cumin (a rather delicate plant) is often replaced by Caraway in drugs. Coriander is sometimes stated to be the 'manna from Heaven' that fed the Israelites, the connection probably being that coriander is an age-old Egyptian crop. The pungent-scented Hyssop referred to by Dioscorides as 'a holy herb' may have been the plant used in sprinkling the altars, but some authorities contend

13

that it was Marjoram, while another writer associates it with Caperspurge, said to grow among the Temple ruins.

The Star of Bethlehem (*Ornithogalum umbellatum*), closely allied to the Onion, grows profusely in spring-time in the Holy Land, and is believed to be the 'Dove's Dung' mentioned in II Kings, for this queer name still persists in country districts. However that may be, the roots of this prolific plant were dried and stored, to be eaten during the long caravan journeys. One species is native to Britain, often growing like a weed in old-fashioned gardens.

BOTANY

What are now known as 'botanical names' were given to plants from the earliest times in the days of the Greeks and Romans, but the science of botany was only slowly struggling to light through Anglo-Saxon and mediaeval times, with vague strivings at some sort of classification. It was not until the middle of the sixteenth century (1551) that a learned man and devout cleric, William Turner, Dean of Wells, often called 'the Father of British Botany', wrote in three volumes his most important work '*A New Herball*, wherein are contained the names of herbs – with the properties, degrees and naturall places of the same'. With the frankness allowed to the clergy of those days, he stated he had written this book in English as he did not think either the apothecaries or the doctors had any knowledge of Latin, and 'many a good man was put in jeopardy of his life' by physicians being unable to interpret prescriptions.

From him developed the long line of famous botanists and herbalists, including such outstanding men as the naturalist, Ray (1627–1705), whose catalogue of British plants contains 18,000 species, and the famous Linnaeus (1707–78), the gentle Swedish scholar, who travelled thousands of miles in many countries to identify and name vast numbers of plants.

HISTORY OF HERBS

The history of herbs or 'simples' stretches far back into the past or, as William Cole, a celebrated seventeenth-century divine, wrote: 'It is a subject as ancient as the Creation, yea, more ancient than the sun or moon or stars, they being created on the fourth day, whereas plants were the third.'

Though we may not take this argument as literally as did Cole, there are records of herbal medicines from the days of the ancient Egyptians, when bunches of herbs were placed in the hands of mummies, from Hippocrates, the 'Father of Medicine', who in the fourth century B.C. taught the value of plants for human ills in the Temples of Aesculapius, the Temples of Healing, the sanatoria of the ancient Greeks. The fact that of the 400 herbs employed by him more than half are still in use to-day speaks highly of his knowledge and research. Dioscorides, of the first century A.D., who is believed to have been an army doctor with the Roman troops, and who probably visited Britain, compiled a Materia Medica which remained the basis of herbal medicine for sixteen centuries.

The Romans not only benefited Britain by their marvellous engineering feats in building roads and bridges, but during their four hundred years of occupation cultivated a large number of plants brought from their colonies along the Mediterranean. Among these were such well-known ones as Chervil, Chives, Celandine, Parsley, Rue, Onion, Fennel, Rosemary, Southernwood, Borage, Sage and Thyme. They boasted, too, that they had no need of doctors, as their knowledge of medicinal herbs was all-sufficient. And, as plants have a habit not only of survival in suitable ground, but also of multiplying, this herbal legacy bequeathed by the Romans considerably assisted the people of these islands, and formed the basis for the herbaries or herb gardens of the great monasteries which sprang up all over the country in mediaeval times. The earliest English Herbal, written about the time of the Norman Conquest, and still preserved in the British Museum, owes its origin to a book written by a Roman doctor, Apuleius Platonicus.

As the monasteries grew in number, their cultivation of herbs extended, for the fraternities had to be centres of medicine as well as of education. From this time, too, date our oldest hospitals, such as 'Bart's', London, and the old nursing orders, as well as the smaller lazar houses for lepers, the ruins of which are seen to-day scattered about our islands. Several of the herbs mentioned for the treatment of leprosy – Burdock, Goosegrass, Red Dock and Garlic – are still employed in various drugs.

Another surviving relic of those monastic gardens is the luxurious growth of important drug-plants often found growing in the neighbourhood of ruined abbeys, in the grounds and estates of old manor-houses, and even in the gardens of old rectories, probably built on the site of ancient religious houses. These plants include some which provide valuable narcotics, such as Deadly Nightshade (*Atropa belladonna*), Henbane (*Hyoscyamus niger*) and Woody Nightshade (*Solanum dulcamara*). In rare cases the true Mandrake (*Mandragora officinalis*) is to be found, with its twisted swollen roots and lurid reputation. For centuries it was cultivated for its sedative properties, but seems to have died out about the sixteenth century. Gerard says, 'It groweth in Hot regions, we have them onely planted in gardens, and are not elsewhere to be found in England'. A very persistent legend was that when pulled from the ground, it uttered a loud shriek, and whoever heard it collapsed. So dogs were tied to the plants to pull out the roots – and 'the dog it was who died'. Though seldom grown now, a description of it may be interesting. Like others of the family *Solanaceae*, it is biennial, with long, glossy green leaves in a rosette the first year, growing on the ground, followed by tall shoots, on which hang dark purple flowers, and later on yellow, shiny fruits. One of its many names was 'Satan's Apples', for the fruit is highly poisonous.

Its evil powers may be doubted, but there is plenty of evidence to show that it was one of the standard anodynes (pain-killers) and was included in that more or less reliable anaesthetic of the Middle Ages known as 'the soporific sponge', consisting of an infusion of Mandrake, Hemlock, Poppy, Lettuce, Ivy and Mulberry. This horrible decoction was poured over a sponge and held to the patient's nostrils. Such a combination of objectionable odours must surely have had the desired effect!

During Queen Elizabeth's reign, with the importation of many foreign plants, came the 'American Mandrake' (*Podyphyllum peltatum*), which has proved so valuable that it is now included in every Pharmacopoeia in the world. White Bryony (*Bryonia dioica*) is often called the 'English Mandrake' by herbalists.

DOCTRINE OF SIGNATURES

The fifteenth and sixteenth centuries were an age of belief in alchemy, occultism and mock magic of every sort, and it is not surprising that medicine became entangled in these dubious practices. A German, born in 1493, Philippus Bombastus (though he preferred to be known by the more high-sounding Latin name of Paracelsus), first developed the 'Doctrine of

16

Signatures'. Though quite unscrupulous, he was evidently clever, for his theory soon spread all over Europe, arriving in England when astrology was the favourite cult, to be eagerly taken up, not only by 'professors of magic,' but also by many of the more intelligent people. The idea was that every plant is 'signed' or associated, by colour or scent or habitat, with the disease which it can cure; for example, the spotted leaves of *Pulmonaria* (Lungwort) are supposed to resemble lungs, therefore it must be good for chest complaints; Eyebright, whose flowers resemble bright eyes, was held to be a remedy for eye trouble. This 'doctrine', false as it undoubtedly was, survived for centuries, and still has its disciples to-day.

SWEET HERBS

Herbs were required in the luxurious Elizabethan days not only for medicines, but also for flavouring, scents, succades (sweetmeats), syrups, as well as for love-potions and cosmetics, and all large houses had their own Herbary, where the lady of the house and her serving-maids grew numerous plants for medicines, as well as the sweet-scented garden treasures, Lavender, Rosemary, Balm, Mint, Thyme and others. Cottagers also devoted part of their gardens to herb-growing, for doctors were often remote, and village maidens liked fragrant scents and powders as well as herbs for strewing their houses on festive occasions.

Britain in Tudor times developed the art of gardening to a great extent both for floral decoration and for food production, and from this period date the development and cultivation of wild plants and fruits, strawberry, raspberry, plum, apple and pear, into the prize dessert fruits we wisely use so much to-day.

THE GREAT HERBALISTS

As botany became more of a science, and the knowledge and control of medicine developed under the College of Physicians, and later on, in Charles II's day, the Royal Society, the reign of the old herbalists came to an end, though their names and works have remained a very pleasant memory, and editions of their books are still being published in this sceptical twentieth century.

During Tudor and Stuart times, when scientific learning was slowly struggling along its tortuous path, British herbal botany,

17

under that collection of men known as 'the Great Herbalists', was at its peak.

Twenty-seven years after the publication of Turner's Herbal, *A Nieuwe Herball, or Historie of Plantes* was translated from a book written by the famous Dutch doctor, Rambert Dodoens, by a well-known Oxford man, Henry Lyte, appreciated more now for the fact that he founded one of the earliest Botanic Gardens at Oxford. This 'Historie' was quite eclipsed in 1597 by a massive work written by the best known of all our English herbalists, John Gerard (1545–1607). Even though he borrowed much of his information from Dodoens, the book is written in such a fresh and vigorous style, introducing many of the plants 'from the New Lande called America' that it makes fascinating reading. Though he was Chairman of the Barber Surgeons' Company, he seems to have been much more interested in horticulture than in medicine.

In the dedication to his patron, Lord Burleigh, he modestly remarks: 'I have added from forreine places all the varietie of herbes and floures that I might in any way obtain, I have laboured with the soil to make it fit for plants, and with the plantes that they might delight in the soile'. This work, *The Herball or General Historie of Plantes*, contained 1,800 woodcuts, that representing the potato being believed to be the first drawing of this plant ever published. He also mentions 'Apples of Love', which apparently gained their name from the yellow variety bearing some supposed similarity to the golden apples of the Hesperides. The name 'Tomato' was given much later.

He faithfully catalogued all the plants he grew in his Physick Garden in Fetter Lane in another book, and it was probably the fame of this garden and other herb-gardens that finally decided the Society of Apothecaries to start the first public Physick Garden at Chelsea in 1673. This garden, through many early vicissitudes, still survives to-day, though it is now under a Committee of Management and acts as a botanical garden for the training of horticultural students. Various beautiful shrubs and trees grow there, as well as a carefully planned herb garden, but one can gain entry through the great wrought-iron gates only by ticket. It is much to be hoped that later on the beauties of this ancient pleasaunce may be accessible to the general public, so that not only horticulturists, but all those who are anxious to see the number and variety of our British herbs, may enjoy its beauty and interests.

Another delightful herb garden, in the Royal Botanic Gardens at Kew, is well worth a visit, both for its classic design and for the variety of British and foreign herbs growing there.

Nicholas Culpeper (1616–54), whose name has survived to-day in the Culpeper Society of Herbalists, was a stern Puritan of the Commonwealth, and is immortalised in Rudyard Kipling's *Rewards and Fairies* in the story of 'A Doctor of Medicine'. In his *Physical Directory* he greatly annoyed the medical profession by a severe attack on their methods, they, in turn, retaliating by scathing remarks in the *Royalist Periodical*. His *Directory* is a delightful and comprehensive book, but somewhat submerged under the deluge of astrology that was sweeping England at that time. In view of modern book prices, one reads with wonder on the title-page that it contains 'a compleat method of Physick – for threepence charge'!

Though his rigid views brought him many enemies, his Herbal so pleased the public, either by its contents or its modest price, that it ran into many editions, and still finds a large number of readers to-day.

In spite of the fact that John Parkinson held the offices of King's Herbalist to Charles I, Apothecary to James I, and was a director of Hampton Court Gardens, he is now very little known. He wrote two voluminous books, *Theatrum Botanicum* and *Paradisus terrestris* (1629), dealing more with the delights of garden-ing than with the medical 'vertues' of plants. He had none of the flamboyance of Gerard, and was apparently quite content in his 'earthly paradise' at Long Acre, where he cultivated many new plants and enjoyed the friendship of fellow-gardeners of his day, including the two Tradescants. The elder Tradescant is interest-ing because his name is retained in the brilliant blue flower 'Tradescantia', commonly known as 'Moses in the Bulrushes', and because he is believed to have brought the apricot to England.

Other prominent herbalists and gardeners of this period in-clude Matthias Lobel, who gave his name to the well-known bedding and herbal plant, Lobelia; William Coys, remembered as 'a generous gardener' and for the first Yucca to grow in Eng-land, in his garden at North Ockenden in Essex; John Goodyer, of Petersfield, one of the few botanists whose house now bears a tablet to his memory, and that vigorous Welshman, Sir John Salusbury, who supplied his countrymen with a Herbal in their own language. Not only are the works of these herbalists full of quaint knowledge and interest, but many of them contain wood-cuts of great accuracy and beauty.

COMMERCIAL HERB-GROWING

From the Physick Gardens of the seventeenth century developed the commercial herb-farms which sprang up, first of all near London, in Surrey and Kent, and then farther afield, districts often specialising in some particular drug plant, such as Banbury in Rhubarb and Pontefract in Liquorice.

But by the middle of the nineteenth century herb-growing had considerably dwindled, for many reasons: wild herbs grew in greater profusion in Europe; France and Austria, and especially Germany, had organised herb collecting and herb cultivation on a grand scale; the United States became a large exporter of drug herbs, and even Japan had entered the market, with a violent undercutting of prices.

When the 1914–18 War swept across the world, consignments from Central Europe dried up, and supplies from the Far East considerably lessened. The British Isles were thrown almost entirely on their own resources, the Board of Agriculture (as it was then) issued a leaflet on *The Cultivation and Collection of Medicinal Plants in England*, voluntary Herb-Growers' Associations were formed, and commercial herb-farms obtained a new lease of life. The Board of Agriculture helped herb collectors by leaflets and lectures, but had no power to give financial aid, with the result that after the war most of the voluntary herb associations came to an end through lack of means.

IN EUROPE

The reverse was the case on the Continent, where the lesson of diminished medical supplies during the war was seriously taken to heart. In France a Ministerial Committee was set up, and the whole vegetable drug trade reorganised, with the result that some years later the collection and cultivation of herbs for medicine, culinary use and perfumery was on a sound basis. Germany, with her usual systematic thoroughness, again worked up her herbal as well as synthetic drug industries under the Bureau of Health.

Italy, with her great flower-growing areas, soon started to

develop again the perfume-herb industry, and side by side with the lavender and other sweet-scented herb farms, distilleries were built, much as has been done in the south of France around Grasse. The Soviet Union, with her far-flung natural flora, energetically attacked the problems of the drug industry, forming co-operative societies for herb cultivation and collection.

In the British Isles herb-farms carried on with difficulty, and no further attempt was made either by educational means or by Government organisation to collect wild drug plants, and another generation grew up which had no knowledge either of the native British herbs or of the possibilities of a British herb industry.

STOPPAGE OF SUPPLIES

By 1939, when the Second World War was beginning to stretch its strangling tentacles around the globe, the contribution by Britain to the herb industry was almost negligible, and about 90 per cent of all herbs needed for medicine were being sent to these islands from the well-organised collectors of Europe and America.

The British Isles were very soon virtually cut off from European as well as Far Eastern supplies, and immediately the Government realised that there would be a serious shortage of vital drugs it somewhat tardily set to work to fill the gap left open by twenty years' neglect of our country's wild medicinal plants. The Ministry of Health set up systematic research into the drug value of native and cultivated herbs, and in 1940 enlisted the help, first of all, of the countrywomen's organisation, the National Federation of Women's Institutes, with its 6000 branches. Very soon other national voluntary bodies, such as the W.V.S., Boy Scouts and Girl Guides, were roped in, and it was quickly found that the age-old interest and delight in herbs still existed among the country people. Many expressed a keen desire and eager spirit to know more about British wild medicinal plants and once again to go herborising in the fields, meadows and woods.

A National Herb Organiser, Dr R. A. Butcher, Ph.D., B.Sc., F.L.S., was appointed, and through his energy and enthusiasm numbers of willing collectors were organised into County Herb Committees.

As education was first priority among the rather bewildered

army of herb-gatherers, Dr Butcher drew up a definite scheme of a long-term plan for the gathering, drying and marketing of herbs, issuing this to committees. He also circulated monthly memoranda dealing with identification of and methods of gathering a number of plants of first and secondary importance, and in between times travelled throughout the British Isles to guide and direct the ever-growing band of herb enthusiasts. Through all the war years until 1945 Dr Butcher acted as a vigilant and untiring organiser.

NATIONAL COLLECTIONS

Over ten tons of a somewhat miscellaneous variety of herbs were collected in 1941, but drying-places were difficult to find, and transport was naturally slow. Organisation did not really get going until 1942, when the Vegetable Drugs Committee of the Ministry of Supply took over the work. A scheme was now drawn up simplifying many of the difficulties of herb-collecting and proposing a plan for financial aid in the way of loans. This scheme worked so well that 1942 was a record year for the young British herb industry.

A national appeal was sent out for 100 tons of dried nettles, mostly for camouflage purposes, for which the deep green juice of the Nettle leaves is particularly suitable, with the remarkable result that 90 tons were sent to the manufacturers. Only those who have gathered and dried even a pound of this flimsy-leaved, uncomfortable plant will realise the tremendous effort required to amass even one ton. And a point worth remembering in herb-gathering is that 8 lb. of fresh leaves will result in less than 1 lb. of the dried article.

PROGRESS

By 1943 every county had its own Herb Committee, and all carried on until the end of 1945, some still remaining until 1946 mainly for the purpose of Rose-hip collection.

During the five years of war over 750 tons of dried herbs and 2,000 tons of Rose-hips were gathered, as well as 1,000 tons of Horse Chestnuts in 1943 – a noble and most exhausting task. Though collectors were paid small sums by drug firms, the bulk of the work was voluntary, and a large number of organisations, as well as school children, Service men and women, and nursing associations, helped in the good though somewhat strenuous task.

As time went on it was found that the simplest method was for counties, as far as possible, to specialise in the gathering of those plants particularly plentiful in their own areas: Wales and the western counties collecting most of the Foxglove leaves and seed, Rutland and Sussex gathering the largest amount of Belladonna (Rutland alone collected 4 tons of Belladonna leaf); the northern counties fulfilled their target for Sphagnum moss; Colchicum corms and seeds coming mainly from the chalky western districts, Male Fern from Northumberland and Wales. A certain amount of Thornapple and Henbane was also contributed, but, as the Ministry of Supply gave special help to those commercial farms where these two and other important drugs were being cultivated, the wild plants were not so much in request.

Other plants which the herborisers were asked to collect were: Broom tops, Burdock leaves and root, Comfrey leaves and root, Dandelion root, Elder flowers, Hawthorn berries, Lime-tree flowers, Raspberry leaves, Valerian root (here again commercial herb farms contributed largely to the nation's stores), Yarrow, Parsley Piert and Wormwood.

SEAWEED COLLECTING

One of the greatest successes of the Scottish, Northern, Western and Welsh Herb Committees was the gathering of two kinds of seaweed, Gigartina and Chondrus, which provide the substance known as agar-agar, a jelly-like material, almost all of which had previously been imported from Japan. Thirty-three tons were collected in 1944 alone. Agar-agar has been largely connected with the development of penicillin, and experimental work would have been seriously hampered without this British seaweed, gathered under considerable difficulty from the rocky, storm-swept coasts of Northumberland, Wales, Cornwall, Dorset and Scotland.

This, in brief, is the history of organised herb-gathering throughout the British Isles during the war years. Though the Vegetable Drugs Committee no longer directs the utilisation of our wild-drug plants, for some years to come there will still be a big demand for Rose-hips, Belladonna, Colchicum, Male Fern and many other herbs. Apart from the valuable addition to the nation's medicine chest, these years of herb-gathering have given hundreds of people, mostly women and children, an insight into that delightful world of the British Flora. Probably a good many people will continue to collect these humble 'worts', and in many cases will wish to cultivate those savoury plants we used to buy so lavishly from other countries and can so easily and with such pleasure grow in our own gardens.

A FEW HINTS

Though gathering and drying are dealt with fully in the section dealing with Garden Herbs, there are some special points that it is as well to remember in connection with the collecting, drying and marketing of wild plants.

First of all a word of warning must be given regarding 'simples' ('simples' is the old expression for a single herb, as opposed to the combinations of plants which usually make up our medicines), and this is the danger of amateur experimenting with them for oneself or one's family. The old herbalists may have (rather emphatically) prescribed certain plants as beneficial for certain ailments, but herbal extracts are too powerful to be trifled with, and except in the case of such innocuous drinks as Peppermint and Lime-flower Tea, for example, concoctions should not be devised by the unskilled. A great deal of research is still being done in regard to the action of plants on the physiological system, and indiscriminate doctoring with herbs may be extremely harmful.

The difficulty, too, of exact identification of some wild plants – for instance, in the case of the numerous umbelliferous species – may easily cause confusion between a harmful and a harmless one. This is borne out by a recent newspaper report telling of a death caused by the eating of Fool's Parsley (*Aethusa cynapium*), a highly poisonous plant, easily confused with the garden Parsley, especially as it is a common garden weed.

Another point to be remembered in gathering herbs is that only those which are known to grow in profusion in a district should be collected. Time and energy are wasted in hunting for isolated plants, and before setting out on a day's herborising a definite plan should be mapped out as to what plants are to be collected and what areas visited.

Permission should always be asked of farmers and landowners for access to fields or woods; this may save a good deal of explanation later on, and as an act of courtesy may keep the way open for other naturalists. Rules as to footpaths and growing crops must also be respected, and however tempting plants may look growing in a wheat field, they must be passed by until the crop is being harvested. There should be no need to-day to warn collectors to shut all gates and to avoid frightening young stock.

HOW TO BECOME A HERB-GATHERER

One of the most difficult tasks of the County herb organisers was to teach gatherers how to identify wild plants, for country people have a habit of taking the wild flowers for granted, and in the school days of the older people Nature Study was not included in the curriculum. But for anyone who wishes to take up the collecting of herbs, some knowledge of botany is very desirable. There are many beautiful and useful botanical books of all sizes to suit all purses, so that it is an easy – and delightful – matter first of all to read up the subject. The next step is, if possible, to join a Naturalists' Club, or to go out either by oneself or with friends on a floral foray, complete with text-book and vasculum, or metal container in which to bring home plants to be identified and pressed.

Some herb-gatherers speak rather scornfully of the 'Latin names', saying that they much prefer the beautiful old English titles. No one will deny the exquisite poetry of many plant-names, but serious students will soon find that the only way in which one can be sure of collecting the right plant is by knowledge of the generic (group) and specific (species) name; for, of the many plants belonging to one genus, perhaps only one species may be the required herb. This is the reason why throughout this book (and most other books on plants) generic and specific names are always given. The botanical name is the only standard of identity, not only in the British Isles, but throughout the world.

Some of us are rather apt to take the Linnaean classification of plants as static and final, though there is no doubt that Linnaeus himself believed it to be neither perfect nor permanent, and since his time several attempts have been made at re-classification.

One of the latest methods of classification has been followed in this book, and some of the botanical names mentioned here may seem at first rather confusing to those students who have become used to the earlier nomenclature. But all will realise that botanical knowledge must aim at being more precise, and not be bound by tradition, which may act as a check on the whole of scientific development.

MARKETING

Most drug firms accept only the dried article, and as in some cases only large amounts, such as 28 lb. minimum, will be considered, marketing is not always easy. When first approaching any drug firm, this question of amounts should always be made clear, and it is just as well to send samples, even though excellent small samples are no guarantee of the condition in which a 56-lb. parcel will arrive! For dried herbs have the great disadvantage of absorbing moisture, and if too long on the railway, may appear at their destination a soggy, and often mildewed, mass, quite useless for drug extraction. To prevent such a happening, herbs should be absolutely dry before dispatch, they should be packed either in closely woven sacks, securely tied or, still better, in paper-lined tins or boxes, and sent carriage paid.

Should it be found that herbs, apparently dry, have become damp through a period of heavy rain, another day's drying will probably get them back to their original crisp state. But if herbs have heated and become discoloured and mildewed, they are useless for sale.

AGRIMONY

Agrimonia eupatoria, Rosaceae

Waiting for buses in country lanes can be considerably brightened if one spends the time searching for wild flowers. A plant you are sure to find from June to September is the Common Agrimony, with its tall spikes of delicately scented, sulphur-yellow flowers and roughly cut leaves, divided into large and small leaflets. The fruit is a stiff, hairy burr which clings to everything, this accounting largely for its wide distribution. It is no relation to the Hemp Agrimony, which is not so common. Agrimony has been a useful herb since the time of the ancient Greeks, who gave it the name 'argemone', as they believed it cured cataract of the eyes. Its second name is also Greek, in honour of a king, Mithridates Eupator, who specialised in herbs, particularly poisonous ones.

Gerard tells us that 'a decoction of the leaves is good for them that have naughty livers', and for many hundreds of years it was used for curing jaundice and liver complaints. The same idea is evidently in the minds of villagers, who always add it to that mixed bunch of wild plants which they gather early in the year for a 'spring drink'. Whatever its former merits, it is now used in medicine as a tonic and blood purifier, as well as for digestive disorders.

It should be gathered when the flowers, 'Church Steeples', are just blooming; the whole herb hung in small bunches and dried indoors, or outdoors in a warm shed, leaves and flowers being rubbed down to powder when dry.

Common Wild Flowers, fig. 18.

ALKANET
Anchusa officinalis, Boraginaceae

This is one of the rarer plants of the English countryside. Culpeper says 'it is very hard to come by', though it is a great favourite in gardens, especially where there are bees, as it is one of their special favourites – bees are often said to prefer blue flowers. It is probably an alien, having spread from Central Europe, where it has grown and been cultivated for centuries for its red dye. In fact, its name comes from the Greek, 'anchousa', meaning a dye, and it is believed to have been introduced into this country in the early sixteenth century from France, for its medicinal value, at a time when herbal remedies were most popular. Gerard calls it 'wilde bugloss', mentioning rather sceptically that 'the gentlewomen of France do paint their faces with these roots, so it is said'.

But, whatever its origin, it is found now in many counties, though chiefly in the east near the sea-coast, and it was for some time cultivated for its dye, used for staining wood. In the sixteenth and seventeenth centuries the flowers were added to wine to give flavour and colour, and a cordial made from it restored 'those of melancholy and dismal habit' to health and cheerfulness. The dried root of alkanet is still recommended in the manufacture of ointment for cuts and bruises.

Hiding away in hedge-rows or woods, this little plant can easily be overlooked, though the herb-gatherer, knowing its medicinal value, will probably have marked the spot where year after year it will appear. It has small yellow flowers and a much-divided, dark-green leaf, not very much like its gay garden relation with brilliant scarlet or yellow blooms. For hundreds of years it was prized as a herb of great value, as indicated by one of its local names, Herb Benet, a corruption of *herba benedicta* (holy herb), from the belief that when worn in an amulet it warded off evil spirits and venomous insects. The name 'geum' comes from a Greek word meaning 'I taste', for Culpeper says the root has 'a delicate flavour and taste' that 'comforteth the heart'. In modern medicine the herb is advised as an astringent for digestive troubles. The dried root is made into an infusion for feverish colds, catarrh and sore throats, and it is sometimes recommended for general debility. Both root and herb used externally are said to clear the skin of eruptions and freckles.

The whole plant is collected about July, when the flowers are at their best, and in drying, even the slender stalks will crush down and can be included. The more compact Water Avens, with dull-purplish, bell-shaped flowers, is not nearly so common, but is often used for the same medicinal purposes.

Common Wild Flowers, fig. 17.

BEARBERRY

Arctostaphylos uva ursi, Ericaceae

Some of the botanical names of plants are as pleasant as their English ones, but it is difficult to reconcile the somewhat awkward generic name of 'arctostaphylos' with this dainty, bright-coloured little shrub. In fact, in medicine this generic name is often omitted and the herb is catalogued under its specific name of 'uva ursi', but the curious fact is that both Greek and Latin names can be translated into the simple English word Beargrape or Bearberry.

Like other members of the Heath family, it is a 'social' plant, and grows in colonies, spreading in patches over heaths and mountain-sides in Scotland and the north of England. Its leaves are evergreen, turning red in winter, the flowers are small and rose-coloured, and the berries glossy scarlet and rather insipid, though moorfowl feast greedily on them. The plant was entered in the *British Pharmacopoeia* in 1788, where it is still retained, large amounts of it having always been imported to this country from the northern parts of Europe. The leaves are the part used medicinally, as they provide a valuable drug, known as 'arbutin', employed for kidney and digestive troubles.

Unlike most herbs, the leaves are gathered as late as September and October, and drying is best carried out in a warm shed, where the leathery little leaves can be spread out singly on racks. It is important that drying should be quickly carried out, so that the leaves retain their dark-green colour.

BITTERSWEET or WOODY NIGHTSHADE
Solanum dulcamara, Solanaceae

This plant belongs to a large and very interesting family, which includes the Potato, Tomato, Eggplant, Mandrake and many others which provide valuable foods and medicines. Though it is not so poisonous as its relation, Deadly Nightshade, with which it is often confused, it has quite an unpleasant reputation, and children are warned of its glossy red berries. The purple flowers are small and star-shaped, very like those of the Potato, the leaves smooth and dark green. Damp places, especially near ponds and rivers, are its favourite habitat, where after the winter's rest it grows sometimes to a height of 6 or 8 feet.

An ancient name is 'Felonwort', felon meaning 'whitlow' or 'abscess', and in many villages to-day the berries are cut apart and bandaged over such sore parts. At least from Roman times, the berries and stalks have been used medicinally, the name 'solanum' being derived from the Latin *'solamen'* – that is, 'solace or comfort' – owing to its soothing narcotic properties. Bittersweet is now recommended for rheumatism and skin diseases. Unlike most herbs, it is not the leaves that are employed for medicine, but the stalks, and when the plant is grown on herb farms in large quantities the stems are collected in the autumn, when the leaves have fallen, and are cut into $\frac{1}{2}$-inch pieces with a chaff-cutter and dried. The only other British plant of this genus, the Black Nightshade (*Solanum nigrum*), has white flowers and black berries. It is fairly common as a weed in the British Isles, and has the same drug properties as Bittersweet.

Common Wild Flowers, fig. 172.

BOX
Buxus sempervirens, Buxaceae

Box is considered to be a native of Britain, though hundreds of years ago it came from southern Europe, and it is found growing wild in chalky districts, mainly in southern and central England. In some parts of Surrey, notably Box Hill, in Buckingham and Gloucestershire, Box trees grow plentifully to a height of 15 feet or more.

But Box is best known in its dwarf state, cultivated as an edging, usually in old gardens, where its dark, glossy, evergreen leaves give brightness throughout the year. It has rather fallen out of use, as it is very slow growing, needs frequent clipping, and is believed to act as a cosy hibernating place for various pests.

The young leaves are bright green, becoming darker with age, small, oval and entire. The flowers, which appear in May, are small, whitish-green and insignificant. The seeds are tiny and black.

The wood of Box is the heaviest European wood, and does not float in water. It is of very hard texture. Gerard speaks of it as of 'great beautie' and 'fit for dagger haftes', and it is still held to be the finest for engraving and wood-carving, and drawing instruments.

The juice of both leaves and root is bitter and poisonous, and has an unpleasant odour. Leaves and clippings – parts required for the drug trade – are trimmed from the plants from June to September and dried. The main drug which is extracted, 'Buxine', is used as a narcotic sedative and purgative. It was formerly largely employed in the Far East for epilepsy and leprosy.

BROOM
Cytisus scoparius, Papilionaceae

Everyone knows the flaming Broom of commons and wastelands, though it is sometimes confused with Gorse, a closely related plant, which has prickly spines and a strong almond scent. Broom has butterfly-shaped, bright-yellow flowers with a conspicuous standard petal and leaves divided into three leaflets, and is one of the most beautiful of British shrubs. The family to which it belongs provides some of our useful garden vegetables, peas, beans and lentils, as well as such valuable drug plants as Liquorice and Senna.

'Broom' seems to have been its early name, for Culpeper says that 'to spend time in writing a description thereof is altogether useless, it being so generally used by all good housewives almost throughout the land to sweep their houses with'. Fortunately, we do not now have to clean our houses with broom-tops, and they are put to much better use by providing a powerful drug for kidney and liver affections, and also for heart diseases. Gerard tells us 'that worthy Prince of famous memory, Henry VIII, King of England, was wont to drinke the distilled waters of Broome flours, against surfets and diseases thereof arising', which in modern language appears to mean digestive troubles arising from over-eating.

Broom-tops from 12 to 18 inches long are gathered in March and April, before the flowers appear, and are dried in bunches. Some herb firms will take broom-tops undried, but drying is actually a very easy matter.

Common Wild Flowers, fig. 20.

BUCKBEAN
Menyanthes trifoliata, Gentianaceae

One of the many beautiful marsh plants with which Britain abounds, probably owing their luxurious growth to their almost unapproachable position. Though some botanists say this plant is common, it is usually so hidden away in boggy places and around the edges of ponds in woods and forests that it is not very easy to find, except when in full bloom from May to early July. Then, from its clusters of deep green trefoil-like leaves, the flower-spikes rise, pale pink and foamy white, spreading across the marshy ground in shimmering beauty.

Like the other members of the Gentian family, it is very bitter, both when fresh and when distilled. In Yorkshire and the north of England, where it is found in greater abundance than in the south, the plant is collected and infused for feverish colds. When ague was prevalent it was one of the most frequently used remedies. And, probably owing to its tonic properties, it was considered helpful in scurvy. It is now recommended for rheumatism and skin diseases and for reducing fever. Practically all of it used in the drug trade was imported, and it was only during the Second World War that home-grown supplies were collected to any extent.

It is not a very easy plant to dry, for its rather soft leaves are apt to shrivel if dried too quickly, and discolour if drying is too slow.

Common Wild Flowers, fig. 118.

34

BUCKTHORN
Rhamnus cathartica, Rhamnaceae

The Buckthorn, or High-waythorn, is a tall shrub found in woods and hedges, with insignificant, creamy-white flowers and inviting black berries. It belongs to a very small but distinguished family, with only one British genus, consisting of two species, but one prickly relation growing in the East is said to have provided Christ's Crown of Thorns, and the legend is preserved in its specific name of 'Spina-Christi'. A close relation of the British Buckthorn (*Rhamnus Purshianus*) provides the bark for the drug Cascara sagrada. The berries of the English Buckthorn (one may call it this, as it is very rare in Scotland), as its specific name shows, have been freely employed in purgative medicine, and the decoction of Victorian times known as 'Syrup of Buckthorn' was prepared, with sugar and ginger, in an ineffectual attempt to disguise the highly unpleasant taste of the berries. It has, fortunately, gone out of use, being more suitable, one writer says, for the strong stomachs of animals than those of children.

The berries also have other uses: when unripe, for producing a yellow dye, and when ripe, the juice treated together with other substances forms the paint known as 'Sap green'. When required for medicinal purposes, the ripe berries are picked for drying during September. If dried in the home, the storage tin should be carefully labelled, for if eaten by mistake they can have very harmful, though not actually poisonous, effects.

Common Wild Flowers, fig. 56.

BURDOCK
Arctium lappa, Compositae

There is no difficulty in finding this plant, for it grows along the waysides, standing out prominently with its large leaves, rather like rhubarb, covered on the green upper surface with fine hairs, and below with a thick, cottony down. The stems are thick, and the flowers of a deep maroon, very soon replaced by the fruit, or burrs, which readily cling to clothing, and even more aggressively to hair. The Greek name, 'Arktos', was given it from rather exaggerated similarity to a bear, and the specific name 'lappa', also from the Greek, means 'to seize'. The adhesiveness of these burrs combined with the fact that animals will not eat the plant possibly account for its abundance.

The root and leaves have been used in medicine from very early times, Culpeper lauding its virtues for many ailments, from the 'bite of serpentes and madde dogges' to 'any place burnt with fire'. It has always been considered one of the finest blood purifiers, and is now employed in medicine for the treatment of digestive troubles and skin diseases.

The leaves are not difficult to dry if they are spread singly on wire trays and turned regularly. Roots, which are used for the same medicinal purposes, are not easy to lift, as they are tough and go down deeply into the soil. A long spade is the best implement for digging, so that they may be got out unbroken. Leaves are collected in June and July, and the roots dug any time in the autumn.

BUTCHER'S BROOM
Ruscus aculeatus, Ruscaceae

This beautiful shrub used to be classed as belonging to the family *Liliaceae*, known to us chiefly by the gorgeous tulips and lilies that during spring and summer make a flaming mass of bloom in our gardens. These sweet-scented flowers comprise most of the members of this family, but more important to us from an economic point of view are allied plants which produce some of our most valued vegetables, Leeks, Onions, Garlic, Chives and Asparagus.

Butcher's Broom is often planted in gardens for its ornamental value, but it grows wild in some woody and shady places, mostly in southern England. It is an unusual plant, for what appear to be leaves are actually flattened branches. The real leaves are minute and scale-like, and the tiny green flowers grow in the axils. The berries are large and rich scarlet, often lasting on the bushes long after Christmas. The plant has many local names – 'Knee Holly' and 'Box Holly', on account of its sharp spikes, and 'Jew's Myrtle', from some ancient connection with Jewish feasts. It gets its name of Butcher's Broom from the fact that the twigs were once bound together for the cleansing of butchers' blocks – a somewhat laborious method, and far less effective than the present steel brushes used for that purpose!

Both the leaves and root are used in the making of drugs for kidney and liver troubles.

CARROT (WILD)
Daucus carota, Umbelliferae

One often hears members of this large family, in their succession of blooming from April to October, spoken of under the general name of 'Sheep's Parsley'. But, of the quite numerous species, most have some quite distinctive feature and can, after a time, be sorted out from each other. The wild Carrot (ancestor of our valuable, succulent-rooted garden vegetable) may easily be identified by its lacy, blossoming umbels of white and pink flowers, its graceful, fern-like leaves and the clusters of seed-vessels closely resembling the 'Birds' Nests' which give it its country name.

The Wild Carrot riots along the hedgerows and pastures from early July to September, sometimes 3 feet in height. Though the spindly root is a poor affair compared with the garden vegetable, the distinctive scent is much the same, and the pale orange colour soon identifies it as a carrot. The old Greek and Latin herbalists speak very highly of its medicinal properties, and several references rather point to the fact that it was cultivated before the Christian era. It is said to have been brought here during the reign of Queen Elizabeth by the Flemings, from Holland, where it had long been cultivated. But it was not till fairly recent times that the vital principle of 'carotin' was isolated, as a plentiful source of Vitamin A. The whole herb is used medicinally, mainly for its antiseptic properties and for liver complaints. The seeds are sometimes used for digestive derangements.

Common Wild Flowers, fig. 133.

CELANDINE (LESSER)
Ficaria verna, Ranunculaceae

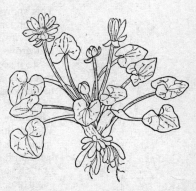

A joyous little plant, with star-like, golden flowers and glossy green, heart-shaped leaves, blooming in abundance sometimes as early as February by the road-sides, on banks, and if given the chance, in the garden. Wordsworth writes of its 'glittering countenance' and, in commemoration of the fact that it was his favourite flower, it is engraved on his tomb.

Its rapid, spreading growth is largely due to the fact that around the roots are a number of small tubers, from each of which a new plant will spring; these are supposed to represent figs, and give it its generic name of 'ficaria'. It is sometimes called 'Figwort'.

The Buttercup family, to which it belongs, also includes the rare, lovely Pasque flower, the fairy-like Wind Anemone, and the Wild Clematis, on which Gerard happily bestowed the name of 'Traveller's Joy'. The Greater Celandine is no relation, belonging to the Poppy family.

The whole herb is collected during March and April and is easily dried in gentle heat. Another of its names, Pilewort, is an indication of one of its uses, and it is also employed in pharmacy as an astringent medicine. Old herbalists thought very highly of its virtues. Culpeper claims it as a remedy for King's Evil (tuberculosis of the skin) and asserts positively: – 'The very herb borne about one's body next to the skin helps in such diseases though it never touch the place grieved'.

Common Wild Flowers, fig. 71.

CELANDINE (GREATER)
Chelidonium majus, Papaveraceae

This showy plant, a hardy perennial, prefers sandy and chalky soils, where it is found growing along hedgerows, on old walls and in waste places. An old superstition is that it is often found near human habitations, like the swallows, after which it is named, the Greek word 'chelidon' meaning 'swallow'. Though the connection seems rather vague, it is supposed to refer to the fact that it starts to bloom when the swallows appear, and ceases at their departure.

It grows to a height of 2–3 feet, sometimes in dense patches, with deep yellow flowers, very tender, yellowish-green leaves and, like the Poppy, the flowers have a thick mass of stamens in the centre. One noticeable feature of the plant is that when any part is broken a sticky yellow juice exudes, rather unpleasant in smell and with a very acrid taste.

According to the old 'Doctrine of Signatures', this yellow juice points to the fact that the plant will cure liver troubles and jaundice, and another old use for it was as an eye lotion. Druggists prescribe it now for digestive ailments, as a purgative, and also for skin diseases.

The herb is gathered during the flowering season, from May to August, and the delicate flowers and leaves dry very quickly. In fact, drying has to be done very carefully, or the leaves will shrivel almost to nothing.

Common Wild Flowers, fig. 76.

CENTAURY
Centaurium umbellatum, Gentianaceae.

This pretty little plant, with its rose-red flowers and sharply pointed green leaves, growing in pastures throughout the country, is closely related to the brilliant blue Gentians beloved of rock-gardeners. Many members of the Gentian family are said to be of medicinal value, and for centuries, even before the Christian era, the plants belonging to it were prized in many parts of the world as a source of tonic drugs.

During the 1914–18 War, Centaury was one of the plants herb collectors gathered in large quantities, but during the Second World War it was classed as of only secondary importance, probably owing to the fact that, with the extensive ploughing up of old pastures, it is now quite difficult to find, and much time would be spent in collecting it in sufficient quantities. The fact that it is also an annual makes its appearance rather erratic. The whole herb is cut above the root during June and early July, just as the buds are opening, and hung in bunches to dry.

The name 'Centaury' was given it long ago in memory of the Greek Centaur, who is supposed to have employed its curative virtues to heal wounds received from a poisoned arrow.

It is often considered to be one of the most bitter of all that acrid family of Gentians – so much so that the old herbalists called it 'Earth Gall', and Culpeper says, with a faint praise, ''Tis very wholesome, but not very toothsome.' The drug extracted from it is beneficial to the liver and kidneys, and acts as a tonic.

Common Wild Flowers, fig. 117.

CHAMOMILE
Anthemis nobilis, Compositae

The Chamomiles, Mayweeds and Feverfews are superficially so much alike that they are apt at first to be rather confusing. One distinctive feature of the true Chamomile is its sweet scent, rather like that of apples, while that of Mayweeds and Feverfews is somewhat unpleasant. Though it is called the Common Chamomile, this plant is very local in habit, preferring gravelly and stony soils. It grows profusely on the cliffs and downlands of Cornwall, making a close, fragrant, springy carpet. It is often grown in gardens, particularly on crazy pavements, seeming to thrive under the tread of the passers-by, 'Like a chamomile bed, The more it is trodden, The more it will spread'. Beautiful paths may be made of it, and there are records of Chamomile lawns.

The flowers are small, with white florets and brilliant yellow centres, and the leaves are much divided. A double variety is often grown in gardens. The specific name 'nobilis' is said to denote its many healing virtues, for it is an old herbal remedy, and country people have long extolled 'Chamomile tea' as a certain cure for all kinds of digestive troubles. The flowers, with crushed poppy-heads, made into a poultice, were often used as a cure for toothache and neuralgia. The extract from the flowers and distilled oil are official in the *British Pharmacopoeia* for their tonic and sedative value. Chamomile is very easily dried, giving off a delightful odour as leaves and flowers are stripped from the stalks. Before carpets were in common use it was one of the most popular herbs for strewing in rooms. The name is sometimes, but incorrectly, spelt 'camomile'.

CHICKWEED
Stellaria media, Caryophyllaceae

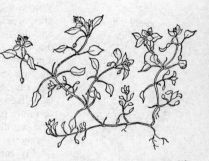

This is one of the commonest wild plants, and will quickly spread over fields and gardens if given a chance, showing a decided preference for the best soil. It is quite a picturesque little plant, with its brilliant green foliage and tiny white flowers, but can very quickly be pulled up, feeling soft and soothing to the touch. The reason why this tender little plant can quite comfortably live through frost and snow is the fact that it can 'sleep' at night and through wet weather, as the older and lower leaves on the stalks have longer stems and can fold over the young topmost shoots.

One can only imagine that the quaint name of Chickweed was given it because all birds, including cage-birds, eat it so readily, and flocks of small birds can be seen avidly feeding on it in winter-time. Poultry, too, benefit from its inclusion in their mash.

Chickweed was once valued as a spring salad, boiled as a vegetable, and also used in various medicinal ways. Culpeper says of it, 'It is a fine soft pleasing herb under the dominion of the Moon', and goes on to describe its many uses for all kinds of inflammation. Like many other wild plants, recent research has shown that the old herbalists were right in esteeming chickweed a demulcent, for it is used now in the making of ointments for skin diseases, chilblains and rashes. Country people make poultices of it for stiff joints, rheumatism and synovitis, and a simple ointment may easily be made by washing half a pound, simmering it with a pound of lard, then straining through muslin and putting into glass pots. If possible, it is best dried outdoors during the summer, as its delicate leaves and stems are apt to shrivel if exposed to too great heat.

Common Wild Flowers, fig. 92.

CLEAVERS
Galium aparine, Rubiaceae

Who would think that this exasperating weed, which grows with Jack-and-the-Beanstalk rapidity around our choice garden perennials, had any value? Though, as we tear it up, staining our hands yellow and pricking our arms with innumerable claw-like burrs, the scent from it is certainly pleasant and exhilarating. The fact that geese and hens devour it eagerly is a proof of its edible quality, for there are quite a number of weeds that they will not eat, as every poultry-keeper knows.

The Bedstraw family (named from strewing bedrooms, not beds) is a most useful collection of plants, many being of the greatest benefit either as food or medicine – the Cinchona, from which Quinine is obtained; *Coffea arabica* (originally from Abyssinia) giving one of the most universal drinks – coffee – as well as the stimulant drug Caffeine, and Ipecacu-anha, a native of the damp jungles of Brazil.

Curiously enough, the seeds of Cleavers have been roasted and used as coffee, being, report says, quite pleasant to drink and mildly stimulating.

Cleavers, or Goosegrass – another common name for it – dries very quickly, losing all its adhesiveness as soon as it starts to become dry. The herb is pulled up when at its greenest – about the end of May – and if too much is pulled at a time, the rest can be boiled and put in the poultry-pails. It has always been held to be an excellent blood purifier, and a tonic during spring-time, and is thus of considerable help in clearing up skin diseases.

Common Wild Flowers, fig. 61.

CLOVER RED
Trifolium pratense, Papilionaceae

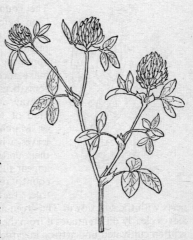

Everyone is familiar with the Red Clover of our meadows; though it may be news to some people that, in addition to its valuable feeding properties when mixed with grass for cattle, it has medicinal value as well. This family, which grows all over the world, and has very numerous species, includes some of the most valued food-plants, both 'for man and beast' – Peas, Beans, Lentils, as well as all the Clovers, Vetches and Lucerne. Very few are poisonous, but the seeds of the garden Laburnum have been known to be fatal. Liquorice and Senna are other useful crops, the root of one being used for medicine and the pods of the other as an aperient drug.

In the case of Red Clover, it is the flower-heads which are used, after drying, for digestive medicines, usually in combination with other herbs. Its main use is as a sedative and antispasmodic in cases of whooping-cough and other coughs of this kind.

The fact that its Anglo-Saxon name was 'cloeferwort' shows its ancient connection with medicine, 'pratense' meaning 'meadow'. It is sometimes stated that the wild Clover is different from the field plant, but any difference in the cultivated plant, of larger leaves and more luxuriant growth, is due to superior soil and cultivation.

The flower-heads need to be dried quickly, as they should retain their colour when sent to the druggist.

Common Wild Flowers, fig. 25.

COLTSFOOT
Tussilago farfara, Compositae

The country name of this plant, 'Son before Father', indicates its unusual method of growth, the bright, radiant-yellow flowers appearing long before the leaves make their appearance. The blossoms begin to gleam on waysides, railway embankments and in any kind of waste places in February or March, and the heart-shaped leaves, with a thick white down on their undersurface, do not usually appear till May. It is often said by country people, and one hopes it is true, that goldfinches line their nests with the soft down. The green-and-white colouring of the leaves clearly differentiates it from the Winter Heliotrope, which is often cultivated under trees in gardens, and is sometimes confused with it.

Coltsfoot leaves are gathered in June and July, and are quite easy to dry when hung up in small bunches in a warm place, such as a kitchen or shed. The name 'Tussilago' comes from the Latin '*tussis*' a cough, and for hundreds of years the dried leaves have formed a part of herb tobacco and cigarettes prescribed for asthmatic sufferers, and during tobacco shortages the dried leaves, by themselves, have, according to smokers, quite satisfactorily taken the place of the American 'weed'. It is also considerably used in cough and cold mixtures. Probably a good many people still remember that delicious sweetmeat they ate as children, known as Coltsfoot Rock.

As this plant grows abundantly all over the British Isles, many tons of the dried product were sent to druggists during the Second World War, filling a very important need. Syrup of Coltsfoot, once included in the *British Pharmacopoeia*, is recommended for use in chronic bronchitis.

Common Wild Flowers, fig. 155.

COMFREY
Symphytum officinale, Boraginaceae

Damp, low-lying fields, ditches and pond-banks are the usual places in which to find this handsome plant; it will also grow luxuriantly in a shady part of the garden. In fact, once it is introduced into a garden it is very difficult to get rid of, as the smallest piece of root will grow. Like other members of the Borage family, it has rather large, rough leaves, and strong, coarse stalks; its flowers are a heliotrope pink, in drooping clusters.

The scent of the crushed leaves is pleasant, and one of the oldest uses to which they were put by country folk was for making an infusion in cases of colds and bronchitis. As so many plants are used for herb teas, it is just as well to know the quantity required: an ounce of dried leaves to a pint of boiling water, allowed to stand for about half an hour or longer, when the liquid is strained for use.

The specific name 'officinale' shows that it has been employed as a drug since the monks grew it in their gardens and acted as doctors to the sick and injured in the villages. And its old name of 'Knit Bone' preserves the idea that application of the leaves as a poultice to sprains, bruises and swellings would effect a remedy. Though it is not included in the *British Pharmacopoeia*, both the leaves and root, which contain an abundance of mucilage, are used in pharmacy for bronchial and other inflammatory troubles.

It was once a popular fodder crop, and is still grown for this purpose in some districts, but opinion is very divided as to its feeding value.

Common Wild Flowers, fig. 187.

COUCH GRASS
Agropyron repens, Gramineae

Many people are very surprised on being told that the annoying Couch Grass or Twitch of our fields and gardens is actually a valuable herb and during the Second World War satisfactorily took the place of imported herbs needed for kidney and bladder ailments. Gerard in the sixteenth century knew its value, for he writes, 'Although the Couch grasse be an unwelcome guest to fields and gardens, yet his physicke virtues do recompense those hurtes.' Probably from age-old instinct, dogs and cats when ill will seek out this grass from among other herbage in lawns and fields, and the seeds, too, are eagerly eaten by canaries, budgerigars and other cage-birds.

As the huge Grass family is a study by itself, identification of this single species may be made easier by the fact that the leaf sheath clasps the stem, and that the creeping underground rhizome has encircling scars. Its sweet taste (many grown-ups enjoy chewing it) reminds one that the valuable Sugar-cane belongs to this family, and the fact that birds and poultry eat the seeds of Couch Grass and some other members of the Grass family is not surprising, as all our valuable grain plants – Wheat, Rye, Oats and Barley, as well as Rice, Maize and Millet – are cultivated forms of various species.

Its Greek name 'Agropyron' is derived from '*agros*' (field) and '*puros*' (wheat). The roots of Couch Grass are collected in spring and autumn, freed from tops and rootlets, thoroughly washed and dried.

COWSLIP
Primula veris, Primulaceae

Among all the many beautifully coloured Primulas of
our gardens there is none that
has the sweet, haunting fragrance of the Meadow Cow-
slip, so delicate and dainty a
bloom that it is no wonder
old writers prescribed an infusion of its flowers as a
means of acquiring beauty
and of removing 'all spots,
wrinkles and other blem-
ishes'.

This spring flower is not so
common as is generally supposed, for it is only occasionally found on clay soils,
though it sometimes grows in profusion in chalky, moist pastures. The name 'primula' is a derivative of 'primerula', 'the
earliest little flower', and is also applied to the Primrose and
Oxlip. The common name 'Paigles' is believed to be Anglo-
Saxon, the pendant flowers being supposed to resemble a bunch
of keys, the emblem of St. Peter. Alternative names are 'The
Keys of Heaven' and 'Our Lady's Keys.'

From very early times, the Cowslip was used for convulsions,
giddiness and 'cramps', and now, under modern research, still
has the same purpose as an anti-spasmodic and sedative medicine. 'Cowslip Wine', one of the most popular country drinks,
was originally made for its soothing effect on the nerves, not as a
beverage. An infusion of Cowslip flowers was drunk to cure
sleeplessness. Only the flowers are required for medicine, gathered and dried when in full blossom during May and June.

Common Wild Flowers, fig. 122.

CUDWEED
Gnaphalium uliginosum, Compositae

This is one of the less interesting of our wild plants, so insignificant that it can easily be overlooked, though its woolly seed-heads make it more prominent during the autumn. Even its habits are lowly, as it grows in wet, sandy places or where water has stood during the winter. Often only 3–5 inches high, it has narrow downy leaves and dingy flower-heads. Its harsh name of 'Gnaphalium' comes from a Greek word, meaning wool or down – the same idea as in the local name of 'Cotton Weed'.

Its lack of beauty is compensated for by its useful medicinal properties. Herbalists since early times have believed it to be one of the finest remedies for quinsy, either when made into poultices for the throat or when taken internally as an infusion, one old writer saying, 'Whosoever shall take it, shall never be troubled with the disease again'.

Its present-day use is as a gargle and in other ways as an astringent medicine – that is, one which strengthens the tissues.

A close relation, Catsweed (*Antennaria dioica*), has the somewhat extravagant name of 'Life Everlasting', probably more from the prolific way in which it scatters its seed than from any superlative medical value. Cudweed is cut and dried as soon as the flower-heads appear.

DANDELION
Taraxacum officinale, Compositae

In spite of its French name of 'Dent-de-lion', acquired probably in Norman times, this plant is one of our real British herbs, and for many centuries its flower-heads have produced one of the most popular country wines. Though one acknowledges it as a most troublesome weed, appearing in lawns and pastures and gardens in apparently never-decreasing numbers, actually it is a beautiful plant. The leaves are deep green, springing from the root and very sharply toothed, while the brilliant yellow flowers offer many a bright spot on otherwise dreary waste places, often brightening the dull grey, gloomy slag-heaps of mining districts. The globular seed-heads, with their parachutes of white down, are very lovely, even though they drift all over the garden and bring forth many more deep-rooted plants!

The root is the valuable part. All parts of the plant contain a milky juice, latex, and experiments have been made during the last few years in the Soviet Union for the production of rubber from the juice of certain varieties. Dandelion leaves have long been eaten in salads, and a specially large-leaved variety is grown in gardens for the purpose, lacking the active drug principle.

The drug is laxative and tonic, and is especially useful in liver complaints. From the root, too, is made an excellent 'coffee', which, though stimulating, has no harmful effects, as real coffee may have with weak digestions. The roots are dug from September to March, washed and dried until brittle.

Common Wild Flowers, fig. 166.

DEADLY NIGHTSHADE
Atropa belladonna, Solanaceae

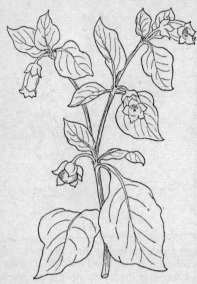

A fascinating and, as its name emphasises, a highly poisonous plant throughout its whole system – roots, leaves, flower and berries. The British members of this family have the unsavoury reputation of almost all being poisonous in a greater or less degree, and it is fortunate that they are comparatively rare.

The name Atropa comes from the Greek Atropos, the Fate who was supposed to cut the thread of human life. Its original name, by which it was known till the Middle Ages, was Dwale, from the Scandinavian word 'sleep', and old legends assert that it was the Devil's own plant, commemorated in the names of 'Devil's Herb' and 'Naughty Man's Cherries' – a polite term for his Satanic majesty.

Deadly Nightshade is a perennial plant, and grows to be a large shrub, with thick, dingy-green leaves, purple, bell-shaped flowers, purplish stems and most alluring black berries, which are said to be sweet in flavour.

Limestone and chalky districts and among rubble and old ruins are some of its favourite places, but isolated plants have been found growing on clay soils, even in the London area, probably carried by birds, who eat the berries apparently without any ill effects.

As its important medicinal value has been recognised for many hundreds of years, it was always cultivated in monastic gardens, and later on at commercial herb-farms.

During the 1914–18 War collections took place in the Midlands and southern counties, where it grows quite abundantly in some parts.

During the Second World War not only was collection systematically carried out, but herb-farms were encouraged to increase their acreage of this valuable plant, with the result that enough of the drugs atropine and hyoscyamine were obtained for the country's needs. Previously most of the world's supply came from southern Europe.

Leaves and root are both used for extraction, the leaves being gathered from two-year-old plants during flowering time in June, for the *British Pharmacopoeia* lays it down that no stalks or coarse stems should be included in the dried herb.

Drying is not easy without artificial heat, as the fleshy leaves are apt to become heated and decomposed, and may lose most of their alkaloid content if dried too slowly.

Deadly Nightshade is a strong narcotic, and the drug is used in a variety of diseases on account of its action on the nervous system, heart and muscles. Atropine causes dilatation of the pupils of the eyes.

Common Wild Flowers, fig. 173.

DOCK (RED)

Rumex aquaticus, Polygonaceae

Docks, with their bright red spikes, may be quite beautiful when mixed with other wild flowers, but in gardens and fields they are among the most aggravating of weeds, with their long, tough roots and hundreds of tiny, wind-blown seeds – and it is quite a pleasure to know that at least one variety is useful in medicine.

As there are a number of species of Dock, any one kind is not always easy to identify; but this particular plant, known either as the Long-leaved Water Dock or as the Smooth-fruited Dock, has various points by which it can be distinguished from other varieties. It grows only in marshy places, damp, low-lying meadows and wet ditches, and it has no wart or 'tubercle' on the large, crisp-edged leaves. The seeds, too, have smooth, not cut edges. Sometimes it grows to a height of 3–4 feet, and is found only in the colder, more northerly parts of England and in Scotland.

The roots are thick and stringy, blackish or dark brown. Like all dock roots, they go deeply into the soil, and are not at all easy to get out. The drug extracted is cleansing, antiseptic and beneficial in skin diseases and in intestinal troubles. The roots are dug in the early part of the year, cut into pieces and dried till brittle. Yellow Dock (*Rumex crispus*) also has some medicinal value.

ELDER
Sambucus nigra, Caprifoliaceae

A large shrub or small tree growing in all districts in Great Britain, and having the unusual distinction of being useful in every part. The leaves are divided into leaflets, the flowers spreading in masses over the tree like sea-foam, the wood is pearly grey and pithy, and the berries purplish-black on red stalks.

It makes a beautiful sheltering hedge for a windy garden, though some plants do not like growing beneath it, which accounts perhaps for the fact that it was once called the Witch's Tree. The leaves, when crushed, have a decidedly unpleasant scent, and when dried and ground have been used as an insecticide. The stems, when cleared of the pith, are not only used by country boys to make whistles and popguns, but are also useful to the carpenter; the flowers, beside providing a fragrant toilet-water, give, when distilled, a drug valuable for the cure of colds, influenza and other bronchial troubles.

The berries, apart from their use as a 'port wine', make a good jam and jelly, especially when mixed with apples, and when dried an excellent substitute for currants. The flowers should be dried quickly, so that they remain cream, for if allowed to dry too long and become brown they lose their medicinal properties. To dry the flowers effectively, place the stalks of the fresh young flower-heads through wire-netting trays over sheets of paper in a warm, not hot, greenhouse or shed or on the rack of the kitchen stove. Rub flowers down before dispatch.

Common Wild Flowers, fig. 64.

ELECAMPANE
Inula helenium, Compositae

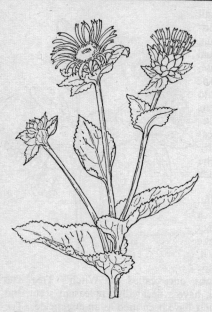

This is a really lovely plant, looking almost like a double Sunflower, and is only too seldom met with, mostly in damp meadows and around the hedgerows. Sometimes it is grown in gardens, where it becomes a tall, handsome plant. Its height, even in meadows, is often 3 to 5 feet, with long, wrinkled leaves, stout stems, solitary heads of flowers of a bright golden-yellow, and a strong but quite pleasant scent.

From Anglo-Saxon times it has been grown in 'physick gardens', and was always one of the plants included in Elizabethan herb gardens, as the root was candied either as a sweetmeat or as an infusion for colds and coughs.

The name is supposed to be a corruption of Elena, or Helen, of Troy, from whose tears the plant is said to have sprung. The old herbalists, through many centuries, had so many uses for it as powder, ointment, oil, syrup and infusion that its rarity is now not surprising. It was once considered invaluable in pulmonary complaints, and still has many uses, for bronchial ailments, for promoting perspiration and in kidney troubles.

The root is hard, rounded and horny, and should be dug in the autumn, when the drug (inulin) is most abundant.

EYEBRIGHT
Euphrasia officinalis, Scrophulariaceae

A dainty little plant, 'not above two handfulls high', says Gerard, with small green leaves, and white flowers streaked with purple and yellow, growing plentifully on pastures and heaths and meadows. It seems to have a preference for chalky districts; this is probably why it is found springing up from the rubble on Hadrian's Wall. The family to which it belongs provides a number of drug-plants which have been known and valued for centuries.

The botanical name comes from the Greek *'euphrosyne'*, meaning gladness – the name of one of the three Graces of ancient Greece, who typified gaiety and mirth. As the plant has been used since mediaeval times as an eye lotion, the gladness evidently represents the relief following its application. Milton mentions it in *Paradise Lost* – 'Michael from Adam's eyes the film removed, then purged with euphrasine and rue his visual orbs', and all the old herbalists of this and other countries held it in great repute, not only as an eye-wash and an infusion, but also as a wine and an early morning 'tea'. In some northern country districts it is believed to be a remedy for hay-fever.

Its modern use is mainly for its tonic and astringent properties. The whole herb, including the root, is gathered from July to September 'and', according to Gerard, 'must be gathered while it floureth for physicks use'. Such a little plant is, of course, quite easy to dry.

Common Wild Flowers, fig. 180.

There are three British species of the genus Chrysanthemum: the beautiful Ox-eye Daisy (Moon Daisy), the brilliant yellow Corn Marigold and this, the common Feverfew, a humble relation of the beautiful Pyrethrums and many-coloured Chrysanthemums of our gardens.

It grows on waste ground, usually in poor soil, merging inconspicuously with the rest of the herbage, and is not very common – nothing like so common as the Matricarias (May-weeds), which are often very confusedly called Feverfews. This name is said to be a corruption of the word 'febrifuge' (a drug for reducing temperature) and long ago many of these plants were used for this purpose.

The common Feverfew is more often seen cultivated in gardens, for it makes a delightful edging, with its sharply cut, delicately tinted, light-green leaves, which last through the winter, and small white flowers with a bright-yellow centre. Like so many other useful herbs, it has a strong odour and taste, slightly unpleasant, said to be particularly offensive to bees. The present-day use for the extracted drug is as a digestive and aperient medicine.

The whole herb, including the root, is gathered during the flowering period of June to August and is easily dried.

FIGWORT
Scrophularia nodosa, Scrophulariaceae

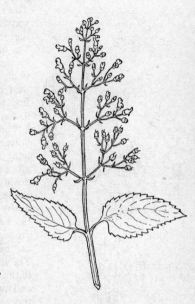

Individually, this herb, with its dingy greenish-brown flowers, is not very striking, but when a number of the plants are seen growing on the banks of rivers or ponds, the effect is very pleasing. Unlike its relation, the Water Figwort, it does not grow in the water, and though very similar in appearance, is considerably smaller, standing about 2 to 3 feet high. It has sharply pointed, smooth leaves, square stems and small, rather strange-looking flowers, and the nodular root-stock gives it the name 'knotted' – one of the marks distinguishing it from the other Figworts. The flowers appear in June, and are quickly over, so that the plant has to be cut for drying early in the month.

It is often called the Scrofula plant, owing to its former use in the treatment of scrofula or King's Evil – the disease which a touch from the King's hand was supposed to cure – and it is still used in some country districts as a fomentation for sprains and abscesses. The same idea persists in its modern application as an anodyne (pain reliever) and for internal inflammation. It is one of the easiest plants to dry.

FOXGLOVE
Digitalis purpurea, Scrophulariaceae

This is one of our most beautiful wayside plants, as well as one of the most valuable medicinally. The garden Foxglove is the same species as that which grows in such profusion in Wales, the western counties, and all over England in shady woods, though it may sometimes be rather finer-flowered and taller. Rose-pink flowers, spotted with purple, hang like quaintly shaped bells all along the strong, rounded, downy stalks; broad, spear-shaped leaves covered with white down spread in a great rosette at the base of the stem, gradually growing upwards, getting smaller as they near the flower-heads. The seeds, which are also a source of the drug digitalin, are very tiny and numerous, and scatter in their thousands in autumn from the papery capsules, producing many new plants for another year.

The plant is a biennial, forming a rosette of leaves the first year and blossoming the second, after which it dies when the seeds have been dispersed. The leaves for the production of the drug are gathered from the second-year plants, so there is no fear that the plucking of the leaves will cause the destruction of this beautiful herb.

The Foxglove is believed to be a corruption of Folks-glove, the glove of the 'good folk' or fairies, though the plant is mentioned in Anglo-Saxon herbals as 'Foxes glofa'. Other names are 'Fairy Thimbles' and the somewhat sinister one of 'Dead Men's Bells', indicating its poisonous nature.

The word 'digitalis' comes from the Latin word for a finger, while 'purpurea' gives the flower's colour, though, as a matter of fact, many Foxgloves are white.

Probably one of the reasons for the continued existence of such a lovely flower is that children are brought up with the knowledge of its poisonous nature and instinctively leave it alone.

The Foxglove has been employed in medicine for hundreds of years; one of its oldest uses was for making into poultices for placing on sores and swellings. Its first inclusion in the *British Pharmacopoeia* was as long ago as the seventeenth century; the drug produced from it, digitalin, was then prescribed for heart affections, as it is to-day. In normal times large amounts of Foxgloves come from Hungary and the Harz Mountains, but it has been cultivated on herb-farms in this country, chiefly in West Suffolk.

The drugs obtained from the Foxglove, known as glycosides, were in short supply at the beginning of the Second World War, but the collection of British plants, and imports from New Zealand, made up the deficiency.

Common Wild Flowers, fig. 178.

FUMITORY
Fumaria officinalis, Fumariaceae

This rather quaint name (often written '*fumiterrie*') is a contraction of the Latin '*fumus terrae*', smoke of the earth, as ancient herbalists believed it sprang without seed from the vapours of the ground. But the whole plant has such a smoky appearance, with its feathery, greyish-green leaves and dusty, frail flowers, that the name may have arisen from this peculiar colouring.

It is quite a common plant, but often overlooked, as it is small and grows low in the herbage by roadsides and in fields, occasionally appearing in gardens. During Elizabethan times it was boiled in milk and used for brightening the eyes, removing freckles and giving a clear complexion, and some of the early herbalists believed it to be beneficial as an eye lotion. It is now recommended for its tonic and aperient properties, as well as for liver derangements.

The specific name 'officinalis' shows it was one of the plants cultivated in monastic times, one old writer reporting that 'it cured melancholia' – a state of mind to which our ancestors seem to have been much subject, judging by the large amount of herbs which they prescribed for it.

Its flowering period is from May onwards, often till October, and it may be gathered and dried at any time during this period.

Common Wild Flowers, fig. 77.

GENTIAN
Gentiana campestris, Gentianaceae

This plant has been recognised as the source of a valuable drug since the time of the ancient Egyptians, for there are records of it on a papyrus found between the bones of a mummy at Thebes, and it was also probably one of the sacrificial herbs which were buried with Egyptians of high rank. Since those far-off days it has been used by the Romans, by the monks of our own islands, and, throughout the centuries, has been included continually in the editions of the *British Pharmacopoeia*.

Several species of Gentian are found in the British Isles, all rather rare; but this herb, the Meadow Gentian, is the one most frequently met with, growing usually on limestone and often near the sea. It is a small plant, 4 to 10 inches high, with an erect stem, sharply pointed, deep-green leaves, and tubular flowers of four petals of a pale purplish-blue, scattered along the stalks.

The old name Gentian was given it in early Grecian times in honour of a King Gentius, who experimented with herbs. There are many varieties of garden Gentians, most of them of the marvellous blue of the summer sky, though *Gentiana lutea*, a large Alpine variety, is of soft bright yellow. As a rule, unfortunately, Gentians are not very easy to establish in gardens.

The Gentian is an annual, and its root (the part required for medicine) is small and short. It has a very bitter flavour, which at once associates it with tonic drugs. Flower-lovers will be glad to know that nearly all the supplies of the drug come from the Yellow Gentian, which grows abundantly in various mountainous parts of Europe, so there is little fear that our own sparsely scattered Gentians will be eradicated.

Common Wild Flowers, fig. 115.

GROUND IVY
Nepeta hederacea, Labiatae

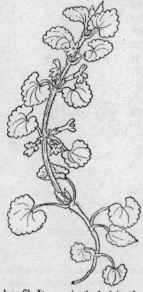

This is a rather misleading name, as neither in appearance nor botanically has this plant any resemblance to Ivy. It is a gay little plant, growing abundantly in meadows and hedgerows, and has square-sided stems, rough, heart-shaped leaves and bluish-heliotrope flowers, which at a distance might easily be mistaken for violets.

A delightful country name is 'Gill-go-over-the-ground'; typifying its sprawling nature, and this name might also be applied to its close relation, Catmint (*Nepeta cateria*), beloved of cats, who roll in it in ecstasy when planted in the garden. Once it was used in brewing, to clear the beer, as hops are now, and thus acquired another name – 'Alehoof'. It was included in the cries of London, probably for the reason that it was considered to make an excellent herb tea, though a singularly unpleasant one, for though the scent of the leaves is mildly aromatic, the taste is uncomfortably bitter. 'Gill Tea', mixed with honey or sugar, is still in use in some parts of the country, and considered a good drink to ward off colds and coughs.

Another use to which it was put, combined with Chamomile and Yarrow, was as a poultice for abscesses and skin diseases. Though not now official, it is recommended for digestive troubles.

The whole herb is gathered during spring and summer, for it has a long flowering period, and is dried without any difficulty.

Common Wild Flowers, fig. 194.

HENBANE
Hyoscyamus niger, Solanaceae

Not at all a pleasant plant, either in appearance or odour, but fortunately rare, though it is sometimes found growing in fairly large patches in old chalk quarries, and a few plants crop up singly in most unexpected places. The supply of the important drug it produces, hyoscyamine, and other alkaloids is made up chiefly from plants cultivated on herb-farms and, in normal times, from southern Europe and Egypt.

Its name 'Henbane' is a fairly modern one, meaning poisonous to poultry, or it may even be a corruption of the name Shakespeare gives it in *Hamlet*, 'cursed hebenon', while its generic name, 'Hyoscyamus', given it by Dioscorides before the Christian era, is from the Greek, meaning 'Hog's bean', as it is said pigs can eat the seed without harm.

It is a tall plant with thick, rounded, hairy stems, leaves pale green, sticky and covered with down, flowers dull yellowish-green with purple stripes, and the whole plant exuding a most offensive smell even when dried. All parts are highly poisonous.

Two forms of the plant are cultivated, the annual and the biennial; but the kind usually grown is the biennial.

Henbane has been used since very early time as a sedative, and was one of the ingredients used in the first anæsthetic – the 'soporific sponge' of the Middle Ages. It has long been included in the *British Pharmacopoeia*.

The drug known as 'Twilight Sleep', sometimes administered at childbirth, contains hyoscine, and during the Second World War experiments were carried out as to its value as a remedy for sea-sickness for the invasion troops.

Common Wild Flowers, fig. 174.

HEMLOCK

Conium maculatum, Umbelliferae

A plant of evil omen, having the reputation in ancient times of being the official executioner of kings and philosophers and other troublesome people. It was the Greeks' version of 'hara-kiri,' a cup of conium being a satisfactory and gentlemanly way of disposing of enemies. Plato, in one of his books, describes the death of Socrates in 399 B.C., from 'Cicuta virosa' (Water Hemlock), a close relation, and mentions the symptoms in detail of how 'he took so long a-dying'. The Romans also used it as an execution drug, but added opium, which they said made the death a much quicker affair.

As it is a rather common plant, and superficially very like some of the hundreds of other species of this family, everyone, especially rabbit-keepers, should learn its distinguishing marks. The Hemlock is a tall, elegant plant with a slender, smooth stem (on which are set 'the marks of Cain' – deep reddish-purple spots), feathery, finely cut, smooth leaves, and large, close umbels of white flowers. A further invidious distinction is its foetid, repellent smell. The whole plant contains the alkaloid coniine, but especially the leaves and seed: both these are official in the *British Pharmacopoeia*. Its use is as a sedative and narcotic, as the action of the drug is to paralyse the muscles.

Other poisonous members of the Parsley family are Water Hemlock and Water Dropwort, but both are found growing by ponds, rivers and in marshy ground.

HOREHOUND (BLACK)
Ballota nigra, Labiatae

This is one of the commonest plants, growing along the dusty waysides or on waste ground, merging unobtrusively into the hedges and herbage. The scent, strong and offensive, and rather like that of Wood Betony, is really its most noticeable feature, though hardly unpleasant enough to justify its local name of Stinking Horehound. The generic name 'ballota' is derived from the Greek, meaning 'rejected', as cattle and other livestock refuse to eat it. It is the only British species, and other varieties, growing in Europe, possess the same objectionable odour.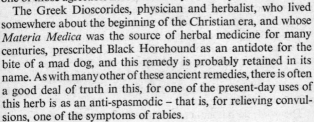

Black Horehound grows 3 to 4 feet tall, with stout, branched, straggling stems, hairy, dusty-looking leaves and dull-purplish blooms, continuing in flower from June to October, and any time during that period it may be gathered and dried. It is one of those agreeable herbs which dry with very little trouble.

The Greek Dioscorides, physician and herbalist, who lived somewhere about the beginning of the Christian era, and whose *Materia Medica* was the source of herbal medicine for many centuries, prescribed Black Horehound as an antidote for the bite of a mad dog, and this remedy is probably retained in its name. As with many other of these ancient remedies, there is often a good deal of truth in this, for one of the present-day uses of this herb is as an anti-spasmodic – that is, for relieving convulsions, one of the symptoms of rabies.

HOREHOUND (WHITE)

Marrubium vulgare, Labiatae

Quite a beautiful plant, with its strong, straight growth, thick, pale-green, woolly leaves and close whorls of pearly-white flowers, giving it a fairy-like appearance – an entirely different plant from its 'ugly sister', the Black Horehound. The scent of the leaves and flowers (when crushed) is very pleasant, and the flavour, though faintly bitter, is quite agreeable.

Hippocrates, born about 450 B.C., the 'Father of Medicine', includes it in his list of 'simples', and since then through the ages it has been in constant demand.

The generic name 'vulgare', meaning common, is rather misleading, as it is found only in certain localities, growing usually in dry, sandy districts – it was once quite common in East Anglia, where it was brewed as Horehound Ale.

It is an excellent plant for a herb garden, partly because of its beauty and long flowering season, and also because of its value as a 'tisane' – that is, an infusion of its leaves to ward off incipient colds. Early herbalists used it in many ways, but at present it is mostly employed in drugs for bronchial and digestive ailments, and is specially recommended for children, because of its mildness and pleasant flavour.

The whole herb is gathered from early June to September, and dried usually by stripping the leaves, as they need quick and careful drying.

JUNIPER
Juniperus communis, Cupressaceae

A beautiful evergreen shrub or small tree growing in chalky districts in the southeast, the northern parts of England, in Scotland, and also throughout the more northerly parts of Europe. There are only two species growing in the British Isles, but it has many relations to be found in other countries. One of the best known is the Pencil Cedar (*Juniperus virginiana*), which once supplied the wood for the genuine 'cedar pencil'.

The British plant is a luxuriant grower, with many branches of reddish wood, needle-like leaves, small flowers and blue or black berries, which are really fleshy cones, and take two or three years to ripen, so that the peculiar sight is seen of green and black berries growing on the same plants. The male and female flowers are usually on different bushes; the berries are produced only on female plants.

The berries are collected in the autumn, and from them is distilled an essential oil, included in the *British Pharmacopoeia*, which is used in the treatment of kidney and digestive complaints and in certain kinds of dropsy. The word 'gin' is a contraction of juniper, as the berries are employed in its manufacture. Only the ripe black berries are collected in this country for medicinal use. They are gathered in baskets or sacks, laid out on shelves or wire racks in a thin layer to dry until they become blackish and slightly shrivelled. As they are rather pithy, there is no difficulty in drying.

Common Wild Flowers, fig. 3.

LETTUCE
Lactuca virosa, Compositae

Many people might overlook this subdued plant, as its various shades of green merge so completely into the surrounding herbage, but such a distinctive herb is well worth study. It is tall – 2 to 4 feet high – with shiny, deep-green, beautifully cut, rather papery leaves, yellowish-green flowers and downy heads. Though it is usually found in the dry banks along hedgerows, it crops up in the most unexpected places, the seed probably being carried by birds – it has even been found on bombed sites in London squares.

Not only is the wild Lettuce gathered and dried for its medicinal value, but it is also cultivated on herb-farms in some parts of England. One of the main sources of supply used to be southern Germany.

The drug, 'lactucarium', obtained from the milky juice of the leaves and stems, has long been known as a sedative, mention being made of it in ancient Anglo-Saxon herbals. In the Middle Ages it was one of the favourite drugs for inducing sleep, and was included in that primitive form of anaesthetic already referred to, 'the soporific sponge'. The leaves have a sharp, bitter flavour, very unlike the sweet-tasting salad vegetable of our gardens, which is its descendant. Though the garden vegetable has no actual medicinal value, it is often suggested as a cure for sleeplessness.

LILY OF THE VALLEY
Convallaria majalis, Liliaceae

Gerard, in the sixteenth century, states, 'The Lilly of the Vally groweth on Hampsted Heath, four miles from London, in great abundance, neere to Lee in Essex and upon Bushie Heath, and many other places.' Unfortunately for Londoners, this beautiful flower has now been driven much farther afield, but it is a joyous fact that during May and June the energetic botanist may come across a wood carpeted with these dainty blooms, throwing out a wonderful fragrance. For, strange as it may seem to those who know this plant only as a choice garden flower, the wild Lily of the Valley is fairly common, and its habit of growing in the dim and often damp fastnesses of woods has protected it from the ruthless flower-gatherer. The wild plant has smaller bells than those growing in the garden, but if transferred to a shady, moist border, the flowers will gradually increase in size.

It has many local names, two of which are 'May Lily' and the delightful one of 'Our Lady's Tears', both due to the fact that by blossoming in May it is associated with the Blessed Virgin.

The whole plant – leaves, root and flowers – is needed for a valuable drug used in heart affections, considered a safer remedy than Digitalin, which is sometimes said to have cumulative effects.

In normal times, large quantities are imported from the great woods and forests of France and Germany, so there is no fear that wholesale depredations will be made in Britain. The flowers are picked in full bloom, the leaves in June and July and the rhizomes are dug in the autumn, when the leaves have died down.

LIME TREE or LINDEN
Tilia europaea, Tiliaceae

One of our most beautiful native trees, so ornamental that for hundreds of years it has been grown along the avenues and drives of country houses, and beside the footways of many European cities (Berlin is not the only large city which has had its 'Unter den Linden'), as the leaves are resistant to city smoke. They are also favourite trees for planting around churches, probably for their beauty. The pale green, almost paper-like leaves, the creamy-yellow flowers with their delicious scent, and the straight, compact growth single this tree out from its neighbours. The Lime Tree also provides a plentiful source of nectar for the bees, and the practice of lopping Limes is much to be regretted, both because it spoils their graceful appearance, and also because lopped trees do not produce flowers the following year.

The flowers, with bracts attached, have been used in many ways for hundreds of years – in France a recognised drink is 'Tilleul,' made from dried Lime-tree flowers, for debility and sleeplessness. In this country, too, many people, especially during tea shortage, have made Lime-tree-flower tea, and find that it is a delightful beverage, rather like China tea. Incidentally, it purifies the blood, thereby producing a clear complexion.

The wood is among the lightest of any European tree, and has the additional merit of never becoming worm-eaten. The inner bark makes a kind of bast, and in some countries baskets are made from it.

Lime-tree flowers are included in the *Pharmaceutical Codex* as a nervine, and large amounts were collected during the Second World War for medicinal purposes.

Common Wild Flowers, fig. 43.

72

MALE FERN
Dryopteris filix-mas

Next to Bracken, this plant is one of our commonest ferns, growing luxuriantly in the northern and western parts of Britain and in Wales, in woody and shady places and on sheltered banks. It often grows to a height of 4 ft. and has long fronds, many-leaved, which uncurl in the spring in a way similar to bracken.

Another name for it is the Shield Fern, as the undersides of the leaflets are covered with numerous kidney-shaped scales, shielding the spore sacs. It has been used as a remedy for tape-worm since the time of Dioscorides, in the fourth century B.C., and is still held to be one of the most valuable medicines for this complaint.

The roots are the part required for extraction, and should be dug from about the middle of August through the autumn and winter so long as the leaves are recognisable. Only large plants should be dug, as the smaller ones may be left to grow for another season.

When the roots are lifted they should be trimmed of fibres and all dead leaf-stalks, and thoroughly cleaned. In some cases they need to be washed to free them from soil. Large roots should be cut lengthwise, so that they may dry more quickly.

MALLOW (MARSH)
Athaea officinalis, Malvaceae

A benign family of plants, numbering about 1,000, not one of them with any unwholesome qualities. The British division of the family are all rather similar in appearance, and it is not very easy to sort them out. A large number of plants in the Order are tropical or sub-tropical, and all of these possess a great amount of mucilage, which has made them important from early times, either as food or as drugs.

Everyone knows the common Mallow (*Malva sylvestria*), with its dainty mauve flowers, crimson veined, and untidy habit of growth. But the Marsh Mallow is not nearly so common, and is a much more compact plant, with flowers rather like those of the garden Hollyhock. The most noticeable difference between the Marsh Mallow and other members of this Order is that the plant is more hairy, and its leaves and stems are covered with a beautifully soft down, while the flowers are large and pale rose. The roots are thick and fleshy, growing deeply into moist and marshy places where the plant is found. Both leaves and root are used medicinally. The leaves are plucked in August, when the blossoms are just appearing, and the roots are lifted during the autumn, scraped of their outer cork-like substance and dried.

The value of the plant lies in its power to soothe and heal inflammation, whether in the digestive organs or in the throat and mouth. Country people have for many years prepared their own medicine from it by boiling the roots, adding a few raisins, straining off the liquor and bottling. A delicious syrup, sometimes given to children for sore throats and bronchitis, is made of the liquid from the boiled roots being added to honey. Another use for the extracted drug is as a basis for a soothing ointment, useful for sore hands and especially for chilblains.

MEADOW SAFFRON
Colchicum autumnale, Liliaceae

This is a very interesting as well as useful plant, abundant in some parts of England, and extending throughout Europe, growing in moist meadows and around hedges and in damp woods, chiefly on limestone. Both the seed and the corm are used for the extraction of a drug named Colchinine, employed from early times in relieving pain, and long believed to be a specific for gout. The fact that it is very poisonous to livestock as well as to human beings has led to its extermination by farmers in some parts of England. It is also cultivated in gardens, and to some extent on herb farms for its medicinal properties.

The name 'Colchicum' is said to be derived from the town of Colchis, on the Black Sea, where its value as a drug was first discovered, and its specific name points to the time of its flowering. Some time in August or throughout September the pale, delicate heliotrope flowers appear above the ground, long after the leaves have faded, giving it its local name Naked Ladies. In the following spring large, glossy, strap-shaped leaves appear, together with the seed-vessels on tall, shiny, rounded stalks; but before the summer has gone the leaves have withered and died. This makes the collection of the wild corms very difficult, unless the place where the plants grew has been marked in some way, and even then the corms are often at a depth of 10 in. or so in the ground. A long, sharp spade is the best tool for extraction. The corms are rather like tulip-bulbs, with a dark brown, scaly covering, measuring from ½ to 2 in. in length.

Where they grow in profusion, as in Herefordshire, the small ones are usually replanted, so as to make sure of another crop, though the corms multiply very quickly.

75

The corms should be collected complete with their covering scales, and will then keep for some time, if not arranged in too large heaps. Soil should be cleaned from them before despatch.

The fruits ripen in June and July, and must be gathered before they split and lose their seeds. After drying, the seeds can easily be sieved.

The Meadow Saffron is often confused with the Saffron Crocus (*Crocus sativus*), which was once found abundantly usually in chalky districts, and gave its name to Saffron Walden. Saffron Hill in London had, long ago, some connection with the sale of saffron, which was obtained from the dried stigmas. Most of the saffron used in recent years for culinary purposes came from France and Spain.

MEADOWSWEET

Filipendula ulmaria, Rosaceae

'Queene Elizabeth of famous memory did more desire it than any other herbe to strew her chambers withall,' wrote John Parkinson in the seventeenth century of this plant, the custom at that time being to strew the floors with rushes and fragrant herbs. Though it was one of the plants held sacred by the Druids, little mention is made of it till about the sixteenth century.

Gerard praises it highly, 'The floures boiled in wine and drunke, do make the heart merrie'.

Everyone knows this beautiful 'Queen of the Meadows', as it grows profusely by the wayside, in damp meadows and around pools, with its tall, conspicuous, reddish stems, much-divided, toothed leaves, and massed heads of dainty, cream-coloured flowers, and a delicate and permeating perfume. The family to which it belongs includes all our well-known fruits – plums, pears, cherries, almonds, strawberries, raspberries, blackberries, as well as the many varieties of wild rose – all of which in their fruit have a greater or less amount of that vital food factor, Vitamin C.

Many varieties of the related genus *Spiraea* are grown in the garden and greenhouse in various forms, and some make delightful pot-plants, with their lacy blossoms of pink and deep rose.

Meadowsweet has been recognised by country people for many years as a useful drink for feverish colds, and is often an ingredient in herb beer. Both leaves and flowers are aromatic, and herbalists employ them for digestive troubles. Flowers and leaves can be dried together, though it is better to strip them first from the woody stems, as they will then dry more easily.

Common Wild Flowers, fig. 10.

MISTLETOE
Viscum album, Loranthaceae

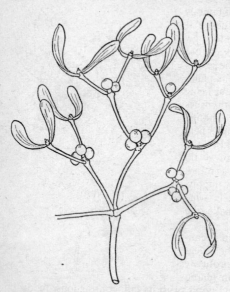

An old Norse legend tells of the killing of Balder, the God of Peace, by an arrow made of Mistletoe. The other gods and goddesses were so enraged that they restored him to life and gave the care of the Mistletoe to the Goddess of Love, and from this, no doubt, arises the age-long custom of men and maidens kissing beneath the 'bough'. The Druids held it sacred, and cutting the plant from the oak-trees was a great religious ceremony, but the reason for this was probably a practical one, because of the Mistletoe's value in cases of epilepsy and hysteria. The Saxons seem to have omitted it entirely from their list of drugs, probably because of its pagan associations.

In more recent times its pharmaceutical use has been recognised, and, strangely enough, the Druids' theory has been vindicated by its employment for nervous and hysterical complaints.

The Mistletoe is one of our most interesting plants, as it is a genuine parasite, having no contact at all with the earth, but living entirely on its host, the Oak, Hawthorn or Ash, and especially the Apple.

The plant is found in many parts of England, mostly in the south and west, the berries probably being carried by migratory birds, though some plants are cultivated. Propagation is fairly easy by rubbing fresh berries on the under side of shoots.

MONKSHOOD
Aconitum anglicum, Ranunculaceae

A gloomy-looking plant with dark-blue, hooded flowers and smooth deep green, much-divided leaves, hiding away in damp woods and shady hedgerows. The family to which it belongs includes all the Buttercups, the glorious Pasque Flower, rarely found, and the many-hued Columbine, several of them highly poisonous.

It is the only one of its genus found growing wild in this country, though many varieties grow in India, China and throughout Asia, but it is often grown in Britain as a garden plant. Supplies of the root used to come from the Swiss and Austrian Alps and from mountainous parts of Germany and Japan.

In early days it was known as 'Aconite'; later on it became Wolfsbane, emphasising its poisonous nature, strong enough even to bait traps set for wolves when this savage animal roamed these islands. By Shakespeare's time it had become Monkshood or Helmet Flower, from its hooded corolla, and one of the drugs obtained from it received its Latin name and became 'aconite'.

The Winter Aconite, with its dainty yellow flower blooming early in the year, is not a true Aconite, and has no medicinal value, though it also belongs to the Buttercup family.

Monkshood is cultivated in this country in small quantities in Suffolk and Hertfordshire; it prefers a moist shady situation.

The whole herb is used for the extraction of drugs, though the root is the most important part. All the plant is poisonous, and animals avoid it. It has been included in the *British Pharmacopoeia* for many years.

MOTHERWORT
Leonurus cardiaca, Labiatae

This plant is one of a kindly family, which, though it contains nearly 3,000 species, has not a harmful one among them, and provides some of the most useful medicinal and culinary herbs, including the Mints, Marjoram, Horehound, Betony, Thyme and Sage and many others.

Motherwort is not believed to be a native of Britain, as it is by no means common, though it is sometimes found in old cottage gardens, where it has probably been cultivated for hundreds of years for its medicinal value. Its name proves that it was valued in mediaeval times, as 'wort' is Saxon for a medicinal herb, and 'mother' indicates that it was used for female disorders.

It is a striking plant, with numerous dull-green, palmate leaves springing from the root, and clusters of pale heliotrope flowers on long stalks with narrow-pointed leaves. It is perennial, and blooms from July to September. The whole herb can be gathered over this period. Culpeper says of it, 'There is no better herb to drive melancholy vapours from the heart, to strengthen it and make the mind cheerful, blithe and merry'.

Perhaps this was one reason for its specific name of '*cardiaca*', 'appertaining to the heart'. In present-day medicine it is recommended as a nerve tonic and for heart weakness, especially after confinements.

ELDERBERRY *Sambucus nigra*

COLTSFOOT
Tussilago farfara

HEMLOCK
Conium maculatum

DILL
Anethum graveolens

RASPBERRY *Rubus idaeus*

LAVENDER *Lavandula vera*

FOXGLOVE
Digitalis purpurea

MEADOWSWEE
Spiraea ulmaria

**WOODY
NIGHTSHADE**
Solanum dulcamara

LECAMPANE
Inula helenium

MARSHMALLOW
Althaea officinalis

TANSY *Tanacetum vulgare*

MULLEIN
Verbascum thapsus

BUCKTHORN
Rhamnus catharticus

ROSEMARY *Rosmarinus officinalis*

HENBANE
Hyoscyamus niger

MOUNTAIN FLAX
Linum catharticum, Linaceae

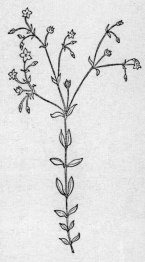

A dainty little plant, with its thin, spidery stems, rarely more than 6 inches high, with small, roughish leaves and white flowers, like miniature Stitchwort, very dissimilar to the cultivated Flax (*Linum usitatissimum*), which seems to bring the sky to the fields in June and July. Mountain Flax is quite common in meadows and pastures, mostly on chalk and limestone, though it is sometimes found on clay soils.

Its tough, thready stems are its only similarity to the 'most useful' plant which has for many centuries provided that valuable textile known as linen for household use, which in fact went out of common use only with extensive cotton-growing in the United States.

The flowers of the Mountain Flax usually appear about May and continue until September, and it may be gathered at any time during that period, but masses of this tiny plant must be collected to obtain even one pound of it! Fortunately it is one of the easiest herbs to dry.

Its common name is Purging Flax, and it is for its laxative and purgative properties that it is included in herbal medicine. It can be used alone or with other herbs of a similar nature. Sometimes peppermint is added to give it a pleasant flavour.

Common Wild Flowers, fig. 45.

81

MUGWORT
Artemisia vulgaris, Compositae

Many a bombed site throughout the country has grown its full complement of Mugwort, and this tall plant, with its numerous ragged-looking, greyish-green leaves and masses of greyish-yellow flowers, offers quite a pleasing sight. It is rather easily confused with Wormwood, but can be distinguished from this plant by having its leaves green above and white beneath, with the segments sharply pointed, and by its less rank scent.

With a reputation from early times of being a 'witch's herb', it was freely used in sorcery and occultism, till in the superstitious Middle Ages it was one of the herbs used by crystal-gazers, as its leaves, 'always turning to the North', were said to be strong in magnetic influence. An even greater virtue ascribed to it – which many of us would be glad of to-day! – was that it cured weariness: 'They that travel, if they carry Mugwort, will never tire'. It is often called St. John's Plant, from the idea that, if gathered on St. John's Day, it gave protection against illness and misfortune.

Mugwort has a long flowering period, and may be collected at any time while in bloom and dried in bunches. The roots also are used, and are dug in the autumn, for, in spite of its height, it is usually surface-rooting. In modern medicine it is recommended for female disorders and as a nervine and stimulant, so one may say that it is still indirectly a 'cure for fatigue'.

Common Wild Flowers, fig. 149.

MULLEIN
Verbascum thapsus, Scrophulariaceae

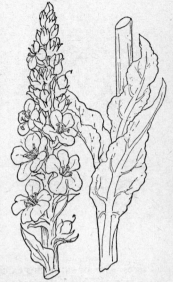

One of the most picturesque of the hedge-plants, with its strong, straight stems, large, whitish-grey leaves and long spikes of yellow blossoms, and it is not surprising that gardeners have transferred this plant to the herbaceous border and developed many varieties of it. Perhaps because of its ghostly appearance, it was one of the plants believed during the Middle Ages to have power over demons. But the monks grew it abundantly in their physic gardens, putting it to many practical uses, and for some years it was official in the *British Pharmacopoeia.*

Its name '*verbascum*' is said to be a corruption of the Latin '*barbascum*', meaning bearded, on account of the whiskery appearance of the leaves. It has many local names, 'Candle Flower' and 'Candle Wick' referring to the use of its thick down for candle-wicks, 'Ag-leaf', from the Anglo-Saxon word '*haege*', referring to its favourite position against a hedge.

During July and August flowers and leaves are gathered and dried very carefully, as they discolour easily. Country people still make it into poultices for toothache and neuralgia, and infuse the flowers for cramp and gout. Nowadays it forms the basis of soothing ointments, and in liquid form is used mostly for chest and bronchial ailments.

Common Wild Flowers, fig. 177.

NETTLE
Urtica dioica, Urticaceae

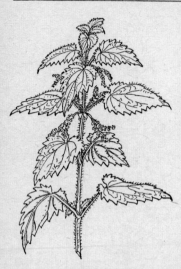

One of the surprising facts about this plant is that before World War II very large quantities were imported, a great deal from Germany, where it has always been put to many uses. When the war began, the claims long held by country people as to the value of the Nettle were investigated, and County Herb Committees were asked in 1942 to collect 100 tons of it. Over 90 tons were gathered throughout the country in that year; some of this was used for the extraction of the dark-green dye for camouflage, and the chlorophyll for tonic and other medicines. This by no means exhausts the Nettle's virtues, for Nettle beer and Nettle tea are two well-known village drinks, especially during the spring. Young Nettle-tops boiled as a vegetable are commonly eaten, and Nettles are an excellent addition to cattle and poultry food, as they contain iron, sodium, lime and a fair amount of protein.

Before the importation of cotton, Nettle-flax was spun from the fibres for household linen, and the stems have also been used for paper-making. Those who have read Hans Andersen's fairy stories will remember the princess who was set to weave coats of Nettle fibre for the eleven swans.

There are three varieties of Nettle – the common Stinging Nettle, the Roman Nettle (rather scarce, but particularly violent in its sting), and the little Annual Nettle that plagues our gardens in the spring. Nettles are gathered from May onwards, hung in bunches or spread on floors or in lofts or on trays, where they quickly dry. The leaves are stripped and despatched in sacks to the drug firms. Gathering, bunching and stripping should be done in gloves, for even the dried leaves cause much irritation.

PARSLEY PIERT
Alchemilla arvensis, Rosaceae

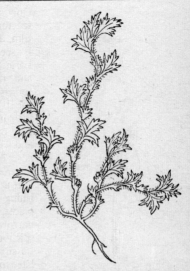

An inconspicuous little plant, growing on old walls, waste places, fields and even in gardens, mainly on light soil. It is much better known by its other name of Lady's Mantle, though the reason for this plant and another species of Alchemilla bearing this name is rather remote. The usual suggestion is that the roundish leaves, with their seven or nine lobes, each daintily pinked and folded along the mid-rib, give the impression of a miniature mantle. 'Alchemilla' stamps the plant as one employed by alchemists, the forerunners of chemists. 'Piert' is probably a derivative of Piercestone, owing to the plant's habit of growing on walls, and also because of its employment in gravel and stone diseases – with great success, it is reported.

Though the plant is so small, spreading in compact little masses on the soil, it is particularly attractive when studied, for its much-divided leaves are of a brilliant green, and the tiny greenish flowers hiding in the axils of the leaves have a beauty all their own. The seed is evidently carried by birds, for it has a habit of cropping up in most unexpected places, even in carefully cultivated gardens.

Culpeper speaks highly of its medicinal value, recommending that 'it were well that the gentry would pickle it up for their use all the winter, because it is a very wholesome herb'. But the method now used for drying this little annual is a more effective way of preserving it, gathering taking place from May to August. It is still recommended for kidney and similar complaints.

PELLITORY OF THE WALL
Parietaria officinalis, Urticaceae

Only a few British plants belong to this family, including the Elm, Fig, Hop, and Mulberry. Its specific name comes from the Latin '*paries*', meaning 'a wall', and the fact that it is called 'official' shows that it was treasured by the monks as one of their useful drug plants. It is the only one of its genus in Britain, and its habit of growing on walls is so distinctive that it is always referred to by its full name.

It is a bushy little plant, flourishing in all kinds of rough places, with bright red stems, narrow, hairy leaves, and inconspicuous reddish-green flowers. Its slightly demulcent properties have for many centuries made it a favourite remedy for sore throats and bruises. One old writer gives a recipe for 'comforting the body' consisting of Nettles, Pellitory, Rosemary and Violet leaves immersed in three gallons of milk for the patient to use as a bath, sitting in it for an hour or two! It was often combined with other herbs for making ointments and even face-creams.

Present-day herbal medicine prescribes it as a laxative and for kidney and similar troubles.

PENNYROYAL
Mentha pulegium, Labiatae

The wild variety of this plant differs very little from the cultivated kind so often grown in cottage gardens. It is undoubtedly native, for its name is found in Anglo-Saxon herbals, and it always had a place in the Herbaries – herb-gardens – of the monasteries. Later on it was cultivated in Tudor physic gardens, and has been grown in many British gardens ever since. Gerard calls it the 'common Penny Royall or Pudding grasse', saying it 'groweth naturally wild in moist and overflown places, as in the Common neere London called Miles end, when poore women bring plenty to sell in London markets'.

It is believed to be the first of all the many kinds of mint to be cultivated. It is the smallest of all these plants, and in appearance and habit very different from the others, with a much less agreeable taste. The leaves are small, sharply pointed, smooth and almost stalkless, the flowers reddish-purple in clusters. The name '*pulegium*' was given it by the Romans, as it was supposed to keep away fleas, '*pulex*' being Latin for a flea.

Pennyroyal oil and dried Pennyroyal have been highly thought of for many centuries, not only for human beings, but also for cattle, and in some parts of England it is given to cows as an appetiser after calving. Country people have long used it as an infusion for coughs and colds. The oil has a pleasant flavour, with soothing properties, and is included in many bronchial mixtures and lozenges. Another use for it is for female disorders.

PERIWINKLE
Vinca major and *minor*, Apocynaceae

These are the only two British plants belonging to this family, and there is little difference between them except in size. The Lesser Periwinkle is the kind more often growing wild, the Larger Periwinkle probably being cultivated and a garden escape when found in fields.

Though some botanists claim that it is not a native, pointing to the fact that it seldom seeds here, it has been grown in Britain for many hundreds of years, and is mentioned by Chaucer, 'Fresh pervenke rich of hew'. It is one of those delightful plants which keep their glossy leaves throughout the year and are not at all affected by the weather, however cold and frosty it may be.

Propagation is by its long, trailing rooting-stems, as anyone knows only too well who has introduced it into the garden. The unique blue flowers have a cheerful habit of blooming at almost any season of the year.

Country people have long used it in making soothing ointments for skin inflammations, but its present use is mainly as a tonic and in intestinal troubles. The leaves are plucked when fully grown, and dried on wire trays in warmth. They are not very easy to dry, as they have a tendency to curl up, with the outer edges brittle, and the inner part still damp. There are many beautiful tropical plants and shrubs of this family, including the brilliant Oleander; some of them are highly poisonous.

PIMPERNEL (SCARLET)
Anagallis arvensis, Primulaceae

As soon as the corn harvest is cut, this brilliant little plant is seen growing in the fields. Its generic name, *'anagallis'*, comes from a Greek word indicating 'pleasure', and it certainly is with real joy that one notices this tiny plant, though perhaps its intense red blossoms, quite unlike any other red or scarlet flower, are the reason for our delight.

One very reluctantly pulls it up from the garden, where it will spring up each year quite as happily as in the meadows and fields. Its local names, 'Poor Man's Weather-Glass' and 'Shepherd's Barometer', indicate its habit of closing its blossoms when rain is coming.

The leaves are tiny, smooth, deep green with purple spots beneath, and the stems that bear the flowers are upright in bloom, but turn backwards when seed-pods begin to form.

In the Middle Ages it was used, in conjunction with other flowers, as a complexion beautifier, there being probably some abstruse connection between the red of the cheeks and the red of the blossoms. Its modern use is much more prosaic, as it is employed in kidney and liver medicines. The whole herb is gathered for drying from June to August, and it is one of those pleasant herbs that dries quite easily.

Common Wild Flowers, fig. 120.

PLANTAIN
Plantago major, Plantaginaceae

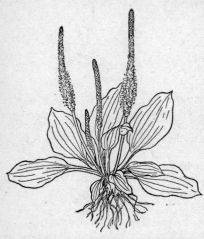

What this plant lacks in beauty it makes up for by its many and varied qualities. In Australia and New Zealand it is known as the 'Englishman's Foot', for the tale is that wherever the Englishman has gone, there has the Plantain taken root. If this is true, there cannot be many spots in the world where the Plantain does not grow! Everyone with a garden knows this plant, for it has a most exasperating habit of growing on lawns, and even after extraction, its flat rosette of leaves and tough root leave a hole which is long in filling up.

When examined closely, its pinkish spikes of flowers are quite pretty, but the resulting collection of seed is neither pretty nor useful to the gardener, though an important part of bird-seed mixtures. Wild birds, too, can be seen greedily eating the ripe fruits.

Years ago, when this land of ours, according to old herbalists, must have harboured many strange and unpleasant creatures, its juice cured 'the bitings of scorpions and serpents and of a madde dogge'. In the U.S.A. it is still called Snakeweed.

The fact is that the plant, and especially the leaves, contain a soothing mucilage, somewhat similar to Linseed, and the application even of the bruised leaves has a beneficial effect.

Common Wild Flowers, fig. 124.

RASPBERRY
Rubus idaeus, Rosaceae

Among the limestone hills and mountains of Wales and other parts of Britain the wild Raspberry grows in abundance, and the fruit, though smaller, is in flavour no different from that of the cultivated variety. In fact, the Raspberry of the woods and hills is often sweeter and more delicate in taste than the large elegant fruits of the garden. The habit of growth – with tall, erect shoots 3 to 5 feet high, slightly prickly stems, a large number of suckers, and leaves coarsely toothed, green above and white below, is exactly similar. Like the garden Raspberry, the wild variety is sometimes found with red, sometimes with amber fruit.

For many years the village midwife had encouraged her patients to drink an infusion of Raspberry leaves so as to make childbirth easy, but as time went on this was largely superseded by imported drugs. When these were unobtainable at the beginning of the Second World War, research was carried out with Raspberry leaves, and it was discovered that Raspberry-leaf 'tea' was no 'old wives' tale', but contained a valuable principle, fragarine, which definitely acted on the pelvic muscles of the mother at childbirth with a most beneficial effect.

The drug will probably be entered in the *British Pharmacopoeia*, and is now in general use in Welfare Clinics and obstetric medicine. The leaves are easily dried at any time during the summer while they remain green and in good condition. Blackberry and Strawberry leaves also have medicinal properties.

SANICLE
Sanicula europaea, Umbelliferae

There is a country legend that this plant's uncommon name is derived from Saint Nicholas, one of the early saints associated with medicine, but another suggestion is that the word is a derivative of the Latin verb '*sano*' – I heal. Whatever the actual meaning of the name, both these ideas bear out the old saying, 'He who keeps sanicle laughs at the doctor'.

It is a small herb, barely a foot high, the only one of its genus, but, as its specific name shows, it grows throughout Europe, mostly in the south and central parts. Sanicle is quite a common plant throughout the British Isles, growing in abundance in woods, thickets and damp, shady places, its little bright, starry flowers lighting up the dense shade. The leaves are glossy, dark green and rather divided, the stems are reddish and furrowed and the pinkish-white flowers are in irregular umbels followed by burrlike seeds, which cling to everything. This is one of the herbs which should be gathered only on a dry day from June to August.

Its use for many years was as a vulnerary – that is, for healing wounds – and though modern medicine does not now consider it as a cure-all, it is recommended as a blood purifier and an astringent medicine for strengthening the tissues.

Common Wild Flowers, fig. 132.

ST JOHN'S WORT
Hypericum perforatum, Hypericaceae

'Wort' is an Anglo-Saxon name for a medicinal herb, and this plant, so common in some woods and hedges, seems to have been from very early times one of those used for curing many ills. The fact that it has reddish-brown stalks and yields a reddish juice, made it in olden times, as Gerard emphatically says, 'a most pretious remedie for deep wounds and those that are thorow the bodie, or any wounde made with a venomed weapon'. As there are now more antiseptic methods for dealing with wounds, its tonic and astringent properties are employed in dealing with colds, coughs, bronchitis and chest complaints generally.

There are a number of species of St John's Wort, but this one is a fairly tall plant with erect stems, much branched, small, deep-yellow flowers, and rather long leaves, perforated with sappy glands. It was once considered a valuable plant for driving out 'devils and evil spirits' – 'Trefoil, Vervain, John's Wort, Dill, Hinder witches of their will'. This probably arose from the fact that St. John's Day is June 24th, Midsummer Day, when certain herbs were hung on the outer doors to drive away evil spirits, and herbs were burnt in honour of the good fairies and to daunt the wicked ones. St. John's Wort grows in most parts of the world.

Common Wild Flowers, fig. 53.

SCULLCAP
Scutellaria galericulata, Labiatae

This is such a beautiful plant that it is well worth growing in the Herb-Garden, and it has the great merit, unlike many wild plants introduced to cultivated ground, of keeping within bounds. In fact, unless it has just the right situation, damp and shady, it needs some coaxing to ensure its growth. Like all the Labiate family, it has a square stem, but an uncommon feature is that the flowers are in pairs, and each pair looks the same way. The deep-green leaves are an excellent background for the vivid blue flowers, which grow from the axils of the leaves.

Sometimes it can be found growing in masses along rivers, by ponds and streams, but it is by no means common, even though one of its names is the Common Scullcap. This and a smaller variety are the only British species, but there is an American species (*S. lateriflora*), sometimes known as 'Madweed', which is said to be one of the finest nervines ever discovered.

Other names are Helmet Flower and Hoodwort, from the hood-like shape of the corolla. This plant's name is often erroneously written Skullcap, but the 'scull' is an abbreviation of '*sculletaria*', meaning a little dish, from the shape of the calyx. Both the British and the American varieties possess sedative properties.

SCURVY GRASS
Cochlearia officinalis, Cruciferae

The fact that many vegetable drugs have been discovered by accident is borne out by an interesting tale concerning this plant. A ship's crew was decimated by scurvy, and one sailor was sent ashore in an enfeebled condition. Near him was growing some Scurvy Grass, and the sailor ravenously started eating it. To his great surprise he soon felt better, and finally recovered. Scurvy Grass has since then been one of the seaman's resources in times of need. Lemons and green vegetables have in later days superseded it, but its anti-scorbutic properties, due, as is now known, to a high percentage of Vitamin C, have led to the plant's inclusion in medicine for the extraction of this important substance.

Scurvy Grass is not the only herb of this Order to possess anti-scorbutic properties, but the fact that it grows on the seashore made it more readily available to ships. It is a small, glabrous plant, about a foot high, with fleshy leaves, flowers in loose white heads, and strong, succulent stems. This Order not only provides many wild plants of medicinal value, without a single poisonous specimen, but also those beneficial vegetables of our gardens known under the generic name *Brassica*, from an Anglo-Saxon word '*bresig*' meaning 'cabbage'. Other garden plants are the invaluable Wallflower and Dame's Violet, or Rocket, both distinguished by their appealing scent.

Our ancestors were quite willing to eat the leaves of Scurvy Grass in salads, not because of its flavour, for it is decidedly bitter, but for its wholesome effect. One of the recent discoveries in connection with Vitamin C is that it accelerates the healing of wounds.

Quite a cosmopolitan plant, for it is found almost everywhere in the world, with the exception of the tropics. All over Britain this troublesome little weed persists, though its root is so shallow-growing that it is easily cleared away – for the time being only, since it flowers, and naturally seeds, so repeatedly all the year that it is continually cropping up.

Its specific name, '*Bursa pastoris*', is merely the Latin form of the English translation, from some fancied resemblance of the seed-vessels to the leathern wallet which our ancestors wore at their belts.

It grows to varying heights, according to the soil and locality, and the leaves, dingy green, gather like a rosette on the ground, while the long stems bear insignificant white flowers. Shepherd's Purse can be gathered almost any time during the year, and dries very easily, though, naturally, the young fresh plants are always preferred.

Wild birds may be seen feeding avidly on the seeds, which are also included in mixtures for cage-birds. It was once considered one of the most important drug plants of the Wallflower family, and for hundreds of years was employed in arresting bleeding, either internally or externally. Its use now is mainly for kidney troubles, and as a stimulant.

Common Wild Flowers, fig. 87.

SPHAGNUM MOSS
Sphagnum cymbifolium, Musci

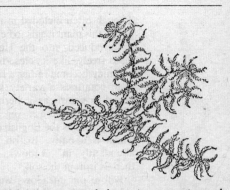

The value of this moss for surgical dressings has been known among the country folk of northern England and of Scotland for hundreds of years. One tale relates how the Highlanders after Flodden gathered the 'Bog Moss' to cover their gaping wounds; and in Arctic regions not only is it one of the main foods for deer, but is also used by the people for medical and household purposes.

Germany is usually given the credit for having discovered its highly absorbent properties some time during the nineteenth century, and Britain adopted it as an absorbent and antiseptic dressing during the difficult days of trench warfare in the 1914–18 war. Quite a little industry sprang up in Scotland, Wales and Devon and other counties where the moss grows, for its gathering, drying and distribution, so that when the Second World War started in 1939 quite a number of people had sufficient knowledge to organise the collection of this valuable plant.

This moss grows in large tufts or hummocks of a pale clear green or greenish-yellow colour. The branches bear numerous leaves, which under a microscope can be seen to be built up of a lattice-work of green cells, enclosing colourless water-storing cells provided with pores. It is this structure that makes the moss so valuable as an absorbent dressing, as it is able to absorb from ten to twenty times as much moisture as cotton-wool.

It can be collected at any time, small pieces being pulled up, cleaned of grass and dead leaves, gently squeezed and put in the sun or drying sheds to finish. The moss must not be over-dried, as it quickly powders and is then useless. Needless to say, before being used the moss is sterilised. Sphagnum moss is the basis of the fuel familiar to every Scot and Irishman as Peat.

SORREL
Rumex acetosa, Polygonaceae

Though often included in the lists of garden herbs, this plant needs to be carefully watched if introduced into the Herb-Garden, as it seeds freely, like its close relation the Dock, and may become rather a nuisance. In European countries a variety known as French Sorrel is grown as a herb for salads, and sometimes boiled as a vegetable. It is not so sharply acid as the English or Garden Sorrel, which is a native British plant and grows abundantly in meadows, especially where there is iron in the soil.

Before our meadows were so extensively cultivated, the reddish-orange of the Sorrel could often be seen among the grass and moon daisies, making a very pleasant sight. It is about 2 feet tall, with long, arrow-shaped, light-green leaves and tall spikes of red, green and orange flowers, later turning to a brilliant crimson.

For many years country people have used it to provide a cooling drink in feverish complaints, and it is often recommended for digestive ailments. The finer-flavoured French varieties can be added, with discretion, to soups and stews.

SWEET SEDGE

Acorus calamus, Araceae

This plant is often rather loosely listed under its specific name of 'calamus', but it has been known for many hundreds of years to naturalists as Sweet Sedge or Sweet Flag – a very suitable name, for all parts of the plant have a delightfully fragrant odour. It was because of this delicate scent that it was used for covering floors, and it is said that one of Cardinal Wolsey's extravagances was the strewing of the rooms of his London house with Sweet Flag rushes brought at great expense from the Norfolk Broads.

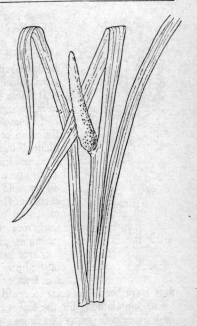

It grows on the banks of ponds and streams, often in moving water, and is apt to be rather overshadowed by taller reeds and bulrushes. The plant can be recognised by the wave-like rippling of the edges of the leaves and the thick, blunt spike of brownish-yellow flowers, 2 to 4 inches long. It was probably introduced into England from the Middle East during the sixteenth century, and Gerard reports he grew it in his Physic Garden from rhizomes sent him from Lyons. *'Calamus'* is mentioned several times in the Bible, and it is believed to be this particular sweet-scented plant.

The rhizomes (root-stock) provide the required drug, and are collected in late autumn or early spring. This is done either by digging the roots from the banks or by pulling them ashore in clumps, cleaning off leaves and rootlets and washing. They are then cut into pieces about 4 to 6 inches long and dried. When they are quite brittle and snap easily, they are ready for storing.

Sweet Sedge is an aromatic bitter, and is used in tonics.

TANSY
Tanacetum vulgare, Compositae

This is one of those kindly plants which flourish as well by the roadside as in the best-kept gardens, with leaves 'like a plume of feathers', according to Gerard, brilliant yellow, button-like flowers and a delightful lemon scent.

It grows in most parts of the British Isles, though it seems to prefer the chalk and limestone districts, and it is often found in cottage gardens, having been planted there many years ago for its food and medicinal value. In fact, it has always been one of the most frequent of all the wild herbs to be planted in that corner of the garden where the sage and mint and parsley are grown, for until fairly recently, it was mixed in cakes and puddings, and 'Tansies' were regularly prepared for Easter Day in remembrance of the bitter herbs traditionally eaten by the Jews at the Passover. These cakes may have been beneficial to health, but they must have been rather unpalatable, for the leaves are very acrid, and one old writer speaks of Tansy pudding as 'a nauseous dish'. Tansy tea is still drunk in cases of feverish colds, and as a tonic in early spring.

It is now used mainly as an anthelmintic (worm-dispelling) drug and as a tonic. The plant flowers about August, and it is during this month that it is cut and dried.

Common Wild Flowers, fig. 148.

THORNAPPLE
Datura stramonium, Solanaceae

Though this plant is an alien, coming originally from Peru, it has settled down quite happily to the English climate, preferring, however, the southern and eastern counties. Its introduction to this island is due to its cultivation by John Gerard in the sixteenth century in the Physic Garden – one of the first in England - that he established at Holborn. He tells us that he received the seed from a friend who brought it 'with other rare plantes' from Constantinople. So pleased was Gerard with this showy plant that he 'dispersed it throughout the land', at the same time experimenting with it in his 'surgery' for its medicinal properties.

It grows abundantly in southern Russia, and in the United States is quite a common weed. Though it is found wild in only a few English counties, isolated examples crop up in fields and gardens, owing, it is believed, to the seed being brought from South America in fertilisers. As this is a seed whose powers of germination last several years, the theory that it is also conveyed in ballast on ships may also be true, and partly account for its presence.

The Thornapple is a tall, showy plant, with a large, white, trumpet-shaped flower and broad, glossy green leaves. The seed-vessel is very prickly, hence the suggestion of thorns, and when ripe bursts open, scattering broadcast its tiny seeds, so that the plant is easily spread when conditions are suitable.

As the drugs produced from it are of great value, being similar to those of belladonna – atropine, hyoscine – used as narcotics, it is cultivated on some herb-farms, though the bulk of the British supplies came from Germany and Hungary before the Second World War. The leaves are also used with other herbs for making cigarettes for the alleviation of asthma. It has always had a place in the *British Pharmacopoeia*.

The scent of all parts of the plant is very unpleasant. It is highly poisonous, and throughout the ages has been closely associated with the Devil and evil spirits. This is indicated by such names as the 'Devil's Apple' and the 'Devil's Trumpet'.

VALERIAN
Valeriana officinalis, Valerianaceae

This is not the red-spurred Valerian of our gardens, the botanical name of which is *Kentranthus ruber*, found growing wild on walls and cliffs, but a much larger, stouter plant often called the Great Valerian.

The medicinal Valerian is a perennial, growing on marshy ground and damp hedgerows to a height of 4 to 5 feet. The flowers are pale pink or nearly white, in flat-topped clusters; the leaves grow in pairs opposite each other along the strong stems, in which they differ from the garden Valerian, the leaves of which grow in groups. These leaves are coarsely cut, the under-surface covered with soft down.

A further distinction between this plant and other varieties is its strong, unpleasant scent, especially when crushed. This is also noticeable in the root, which is the part required for drug extraction.

The name Valerian is supposed to be derived from the Latin 'valeo', 'I am well', while one of its old local names was 'All-heal', proving its ancient use as a medicine. The term '*officinalis*' is also proof that the monks distilled this plant 'in the office', or, as we should now say, 'in the still-room'.

Valerian has long been included in the *British Pharmacopoeia* on account of the oil and alkaloids contained in the roots.

It is a curious thing that other species have sweet-scented roots used in perfumery, and one plant of the family *Valerianaceae* growing in India is believed to be the Spikenard of the Bible.

Valerian has not only been collected in its wild state for hundreds of years, but in parts of England, chiefly in Derbyshire, 'Valerie growers' have handed down the art of cultivation through many generations. These growers collect their 'sets' in early spring from the wild plants in the dales, where they thrive in

103

abundance. The sets are planted out in well-manured ground, 9 inches apart in rows. All flower-stalks are picked off to encourage development of the roots, which are lifted in the autumn. These are well washed, generally cut in pieces and dried in kilns and ovens.

Valerian is also grown in Oxfordshire and West Suffolk, in some cases from seed.

The value of Valerian is in its sedative properties, and it is used for nervous diseases without any of the after-effects produced by some narcotics.

VERVAIN
Verbena officinalis, Verbenaceae

No one would associate the straggly, insignificant, dowdy Vervain with its showy garden relation, the Verbena, nor would one imagine that it could ever have held such an important place in herbal medicine. It is a very common plant, and might easily be overlooked among the herbage of meadows, but when examined closely it has a decided beauty, with its dainty lilac flowers and spear-shaped, lime-green leaves.

It was one of the simples of Hippocrates, the 'Father of Medicine', and the Druids used it as a cure for plague. The Romans considered it a holy plant, and made it into bunches with which to sweep the altars of the gods. According to a supplement of the *London Pharmacopoeia* issued in 1837, it was stated that the 'necklaces of vervain roots tied with white satin ribbon' worn round the neck were a cure for scrofula. In Tudor times Vervain was mixed with other plants for love philtres and in scents and cosmetics, though it is probable that the garden lemon-scented Verbena was the variety used in the latter cases.

It is now employed for reducing temperature – as a febrifuge – and in nervous disorders. As it flowers from June to September, it can be gathered at any time during this period, and is one of the easiest plants to dry. Interesting is the fact that one of the plants belonging to the same Order is the Teak, that tree of shipbuilding fame.

VIOLET
Viola odorata, Violaceae

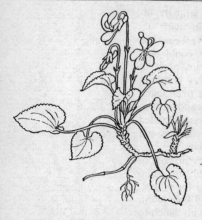

Everyone knows this fragrant flower of our fields and woods, but it may be news to many people that, in addition to its beauty and delightful fragrance, it is also of great value medicinally. There are a number of species of Violet, but the two best known are the Sweet Violet and the Dog Violet, the latter name, often used almost as a term of derision, being given in this case owing to its lack of scent.

The Sweet Violet has deep green, rather rough, heart-shaped leaves on long stalks, and though wild Violets are purplish-blue, garden varieties include blossoms of lilac, rose, yellow and white.

From the days of Hippocrates, the Violet has been used in drugs, as well as for scents, love philtres, as a sweetmeat (candied Violets have been a favourite decoration for confectionery for hundreds of years), and, in addition, it has long been included in all the *Pharmacopoeias*. Syrup of Violets is well known in the drug trade as a mild laxative.

Both flowers and leaves are used in medicine, now mainly for their antiseptic and expectorant properties, and those of the cultivated plants are as effective as those gathered from the wild herbs. Fresh leaves are used both internally, as infusion, and externally as a compress for swellings and for sore and painful throats.

Leaves for drying are gathered in the spring, while they are at their prime, and placed on wire trays set in moderate warmth.

One of the interesting facts about the Violet is its association with Napoleon, who, when he was imprisoned in Elba, said he would return with the Violets in the Spring. Thus, in the underground French Movement of those days, the Violet was passed from hand to hand as a sign of allegiance to the 'Little Corporal'.

WILD MARJORAM
Orgianum vulgare, Labiatae

It is probably rather surprising to those who know only the Marjorams cultivated in gardens that there is also a wild Marjoram, a native of this country, which grows profusely in some chalky districts and spreads its tall plants along hedgerows and sunny places, with rose-lilac flowers, straight upright stems and gay green leaves. Old chalk-pits are often carpeted with this lovely plant.

It is a perennial, with creeping underground roots, and can easily be transplanted to the herb-garden either by taking cuttings, planting them in sandy soil in a warm situation, or, with much less trouble and more chance of success, by offshoots of the roots. It will settle down quite happily, and, if allowed to, soon cover quite a part of the garden. It is very easy to dry, as the leaves are small and soon become crisp. Bunches of it can be hung up in a warm outhouse, or in the kitchen, and rubbed down as soon as the leaves become brittle.

Many uses can be found for it, for it has the same scent and flavour as the cultivated Marjorams, and may be used for all culinary purposes; one which should not be forgotten is a discreet use in salads. If certain herbs are added to the ordinary green salad, a delightful spicy flavour is given, far superior to the all-too-prevalent use of vinegar, which, when lavishly spread, as is often the case, destroys the vitamins which salads provide.

Wild Marjoram is still used in medicines, as it promotes perspiration (diaphoretic), and is excellent for colds and fevers. Marjoram tea was once a popular drink for feverish colds and asthmatic conditions, while old herbalists believed external applications to be good for stings, 'bitings of venomous beasts' and toothache.

As Culpeper says, 'Between this herb and adders there is a deadly antipathy'; and as adders are often found in dry, limestone districts, the remedy will be close at hand.

WHITE BRYONY
Bryonia dioica, Cucurbitaceae

This is one of our interesting wild plants, belonging to the Cucumber family, which includes those appetising and useful vegetables, Gourds, Vegetable Marrows, Melons and Cucumbers. It is the only wild British species. The Bryony is, however, highly poisonous in every part, the scarlet, translucent berries having been known to be fatal in several cases. On account of its large, queerly shaped root, it is often called the English Mandrake, though it is no relation to the real Mandrake (*Mandragora officinalis*), a native of southern Europe.

The local name of Wild Vine is given to it owing to its thin, light-green, indented leaves being rather similar to those of the Grape-vine, and also to its long tendrils springing from beside the leaves in the same manner. But, as Culpeper is so fond of saying, 'It is too well known to need any description', for it clambers riotously over hedges and woods, growing rapidly during the summer, and if once given a footing in the garden, it is very difficult to get rid of. Its greenish flowers leave trails of scarlet berries long after the rest of the foliage is withered.

Its medicinal principle is 'bryonin', derived from the root, used in some forms of bronchial troubles, rheumatism and gout. A popular name for it in many counties is 'Devil's Turnips'.

Common Wild Flowers, fig. 42.

WILD THYME
Thymus serpyllum, Labiatae

Certainly one of the fascinations of our British downlands in the summer is the sharp, sweet scent of the Wild Thyme as we tread it underfoot. This little plant, 'Mother of Thyme', grows luxuriantly over dry hills and heaths, making a soft, springy turf, visited by swarms of bees flying from one tiny flower to another. Its specific name, '*serpyllum*', refers to its creeping, prostrate method of growth, one marked difference between it and the garden Thyme (*Thymus vulgaris*), which is upright in form.

Wild Thyme grows all over the world, even clambering part of the way up the Alps, for it delights in stony, mountainous regions. For hundreds of years its essential oils have been used, combined with other less pungent scented herbs and flowers, in the making of perfumes. The Greeks and Romans, who appear to have had an extravagant love of scents, flavoured their wine with the Wild Thyme, as well as rose-petals, lilies and violets, and in Elizabethan days Wild Thyme was spread on the floors with other sweet-smelling herbs mixed with rushes.

In more modern days Wild Thyme has found a useful place in medicine, mainly for digestive and bronchial ailments, and to give a more pleasant taste to other drugs. The Romans believed Mother of Thyme to be a remedy for melancholy, and Culpeper says, 'It is a certain remedy for that troublesome complaint, the nightmare' – probably by reason of its soothing effects on the digestion. The herb is cut during the flowering period, from June to August, dried in bunches, and leaves and flowers rubbed from the woody stems.

Common Wild Flowers, fig. 192.

109

WOOD SAGE
Teucrium scorodonia, Labiatae

An unobtrusive but beautiful plant, both in form and colour, to be found almost everywhere, though it prefers the dim shade of woods and hedgerows; but is often met with on heaths among the broom and gorse. It will also add delight and colour to a herb garden.

The name 'Sage' is not very suitable, as it is quite unlike the garden Sages in appearance and has none of their strong, crisp scent. The leaves are palish green, heart-shaped, wrinkled and downy, and the delicate flowers are yellowish-green in long spikes. The generic name '*Teucrium*' comes from Teucer, an ancient King of Troy, who is said to have been the first to experiment with it in medicine. The specific name '*scorodonia*' is derived from the Greek word for garlic, and the plant is often called the Garlic Sage, either from its acrid flavour or the fact that it is found growing with the wild garlic in woods.

For hundreds of years it has been treasured in country lore as a valuable medicine to be used in fevers, colds and internal inflammation. Its modern use is mainly as a tonic and for reducing temperature. In the leisurely days of long ago, when households brewed their own beer, the leaves of the Wood Sage were employed for clearing it. The herb is collected in May, June and July, and is little trouble to dry.

Common Wild Flowers, fig. 189.

WOOD BETONY
Stachys betonica, Labiatae

One of our more common flowers growing in woods, hedgerows and even gardens, and sometimes before it is seen its peculiar aroma will be noticed. With its spikes of uncommon maroon flowers and rather sparse, dark-green leaves, it is quite an ornamental plant, but a most troublesome weed if it is once allowed to find its way into rock-gardens or herbaceous borders.

It was always grown in monastic herb-gardens, for its virtues were many, and the legend that it was cultivated in country churchyards seems to be true, as it is still often found around old churches and ruined abbeys. The reason for its cultivation in these places is that it was considered a sure charm against 'evil spirits, witches and the forces of darkness', and its old name of Bishopswort again affirms its ecclesiastical connections.

There are several species of Stachys, all known as Woundwort, for, as Culpeper writes in his 'English Physician' of 1652: 'It is a very precious herb, and most fitting to be kept in a man's house, both in syrup, conserve, oil, ointment and plaister'. Betony is still used by herbalists for digestive and rheumatic troubles, and as an ointment, with other less strongly scented plants. The whole herb is gathered from June to August, tied in bunches and easily dried.

WORMWOOD
Artemisia absinthium, Compositae

This plant is often confused by herb collectors with Mugwort, another of the Artemisias, but there are several differences – its tendency to bushiness, its silkiness of leaf on both upper and under surfaces, and the yellowish flowers, larger than those of Mugwort. It has been known since Greek times as a valuable herb, and in the Middle Ages was one of the plants hung outside doors to keep away evil spirits. Another of its supposed merits was to prevent drunkenness, though in later times it was infused in alcohol to make that highly intoxicating French liqueur, Absinthe. For many years it has been recognised by country people, probably because of its extremely bitter taste, as a tonic, a use to which druggists still put it to-day. But its greatest value is as an anthelmintic – that is, for the expulsion of intestinal worms.

It owes its name 'Artemisia' to Artemis, the Greek goddess of Beauty, who is said to have benefited by it so much that she gave it her own name instead of the earlier one of '*Parthenis*'. *Absinthium* is a compound of two Greek words, meaning 'destitute of delight', probably because of its rank smell and acutely bitter taste – in fact, the expression 'as bitter as wormwood' seems decidedly accurate to those who have been daring enough to nibble a leaf. Another not very flattering name is 'Old Woman', as distinct from the 'Old Man' of Southernwood.

The whole herb, including the seeds and root, is used for extraction, and is official in the *British Pharmacopoeia*, together with the closely allied plant, Sea Wormwood, *Artemisia maritima*. The leaves are quite easy to dry, as they are small and much divided, but the root is a different matter, being long and tapering.

YARROW
Achillea millefolium, Compositae

Spreading along the hedgerows, overflowing into the meadows, the Yarrow is a well-known plant to everyone in the countryside. At first sight it is not very attractive, with its flat heads of rather dingy white flowers, long, sparsely-leaved stems and much-divided leaves, and farmers call it 'a pestilent weed'.

The quaint name of Yarrow is said to be derived from the Anglo-Saxon '*gaerwe*', and Milfoil (which it is frequently called) is merely a derivative of its specific name '*Millefolium*', literally 'thousand leaves'. *Achillea* is derived from Achilles, who is said to have saved the lives of his soldiers in battle by staunching their wounds with this herb. But whoever may first have included the Yarrow among medicinal herbs, it has retained its place throughout the centuries, and has always ranked as a vulnerary – that is, as useful for arresting bleeding. One of its oldest names is 'Staunch Weed'.

Others of its medicinal properties are as a tonic, stimulant and for feverish colds, while the rumour still lingers in some country places that an ointment made from it will prevent baldness.

A pink or even deep-rose variety may sometimes be found, probably a garden escape, for several varieties of Achillea are grown in herbaceous borders. The whole plant is cut and gathered from June to September, and hung up by its long stalks to dry.

Common Wild Flowers, fig. 151.

THE ROMANCE OF THE ROSE

No book on British herbs would be complete without a record of that newest of all herbs to be admitted to the Ancient and Honourable Company of Herbs of Grace – the fruit of the Wild Rose, so astoundingly rich in life-giving virtues.

Of all the flowers loved by the British people, the Rose has always held first place, and no flower has been more famed in song and story. From time immemorial it has been closely inter-woven with history, from the days of the Greeks and Romans, who scented their houses and temples luxuriantly with its petals, and even bathed in a foam of red rose-blossoms. It is said that Roman nobles spent a small fortune entertaining their emperors in rooms strewn with rose-petals, while the same delicate blooms bestrewed furniture and cushions, hung in wreaths on walls, round the necks of their guests, and even entered into the dishes spread across the rose-adorned tables.

The home of the Rose, long ago, was in Persia and India; from there it travelled by way of Syria to the Greek and Roman States on the Mediterranean shores, gathering on its journey one of its oldest names, the Damask Rose, or *Rosa damascena*, probably derived from Damascus, one of the world's most ancient cities, then surrounded by a land of plenty where glorious flowers and fruit abounded.

The Romans, among the world's earliest gardeners, were not content with the limited number of Roses coming from the East, for they developed many beautiful and larger varieties. Horace writes of methods of growing roses in beds (*Rosa gallica*, now often used in medicine, was one of these), and Pliny gives suggestions for their cultivation.

From the Romans comes the custom of crowning brides with roses, connected, no doubt, with the rose garlands flung around their goddesses Flora and Hymen. A somewhat baser use was the habit of nobles of wearing rose-wreaths at banquets as a preventive of drunkenness. The Romans, among the world's first realists, generally had a practical reason for all their apparently sentimental ceremonies.

On their conquering way across Europe, the Romans brought the Rose to France, incidentally founding that country's most lucrative perfume industry, and so to England. But there is little doubt that the 'English Rose', the Wild or Dog Rose, and kindred species, are true natives of this country. The blossom has been worn as a royal badge since the thirteenth century, and was incorporated into the crests of such royal Orders as those of the Garter and the Bath. The British Crusaders, with that home-longing so inborn in Englishmen, during their sojourn of a century or more in the Holy Land, sculptured the Rose on the forts and castles they built in Palestine and Syria. Later the Yorkist–Lancastrian Civil War was fought under the sign of the White and Red Rose.

In Tudor times the Rose was safely enshrined as our national emblem, later to appear on coinage, the royal arms, and finally on stamps and car licences. The decorative ceilings of Elizabethan and Stuart days often bore a Rose in the centre; this is said to have arisen from the old custom of suspending one of the blooms over the table when secret conferences were being held. The Jacobites, quick to use any dramatic gesture for their campaigns, held their meetings 'under the rose', or, in the Latin equivalent, '*sub rosa*'. The latest association of the English Rose with our national history is its adoption as the badge of Queen Alexandra's Rose Day.

MEDICAL USES

Apart from sentimental values, the Wild Rose and its close associates, as well as *Rosa damascena*, *Rosa gallica* and *Rosa centifolia* (Cabbage Rose), have long been put to medicinal uses. Hippocrates included the rose among his 'simples'; the Anglo-Saxon herbal of the eleventh century, and later herbals have referred to this flower in all its forms as a valuable drug; one old writer says of a conserve of rose-petals, that 'taken in the morning and fasting at night, it strengtheneth the hearte and taketh away the shaking and tremblings thereof'.

The cultivated Rose was early included in the *British Pharmacopoeia* both as an infusion and as a confection, and the Provence Rose (*Rosa gallica*) is still commercially grown in some parts of England for drug purposes. During the Second World War herb collectors were asked to gather and dry red Rose petals, and though these delicate blooms are not easy to dry, hundreds of pounds of them were sent to the manufacturers. The petals have to be dried quickly to retain their fresh natural tint, and an effective way to secure this is to spread the newly gathered flowers on sheets of paper in a greenhouse, covering them with more paper. The British and other *Pharmacopoeias* includes red Rose petals for their astringent and tonic properties and the United States add syrup and honey of red Roses.

Honey of red Roses, made by boiling fresh petals with water and adding honey, took its place many years ago in housewives' store cupboards for its curative value in cases of sore throats and ulcerated gums. Rose vinegar, a preparation for headaches and nervous pains, was simply made by nearly filling a jar with Rose petals, pouring on white vinegar, and allowing the liquid to stand till required.

The Elizabethan herbalists devoted several pages of their books to the value of the Rose, Gerard saying that 'The Rose doth deserve the chief and prime place among all floures whatsoever', and Culpeper also told of 'many compositions, all serving good uses, electuary, conserve, syrup and honey, aromaticum rosarum, distilled water, oil and ointment of roses'.

The making of rose-water, the distillation of Rose extracts and the history of the famous Attar of Roses, once a Bulgarian monopoly, are each fascinating and interesting studies.

THE WILD ROSE

But though all these old methods of using Rose-flowers are delightful and romantic, nothing equals the romance of the Wild Rose during the six years of the Second World War—the Dog Rose (*Rosa canina*), the commonest of all the species of British Roses, derives its name, it is believed, from an Anglo-Saxon word, 'dagge', meaning a dagger, either because of its thorns, or from the extreme hardness of the wood, suitable for the short, stout handle of this weapon.

But it was not the beautiful fragrant blossoms of the Wild Rose, shading from deepest pink to pure white along the leafy hedgerows, that came to the nation's help in England's hour of need, but the glowing crimson fruit, or 'hiope', as our forefathers called it long ago. When cultivated fruit was scarce in the Middle Ages, Rose-hips were prized as a dessert. Gerard speaks highly of Rose-hips, saying 'When it is ripe, the fruit maketh the most pleasant meates and banketting dishes or tartes', and another writer comments: 'Cookes and gentlewomen do make rose tartes and such like dishes'.

117

The 'conserve', or, as we name it to-day, the preserve, of Rose-hips has been made for hundreds of years, method and ingredients varying very little. In European countries – Norway, Sweden, Germany and France – Rose-hip preserves have long been included in the housewife's preparations for the store cupboard, while in Russia the fruits of the Rose have been employed as a food since early times. They have been used for jam and jelly, concocted into paste with honey and nuts for sweetmeats, and form one of the ingredients in the many delicious cakes normally served at Russian tables. The juice, too, is expressed and added to spirits of wine in the preparation of liqueurs.

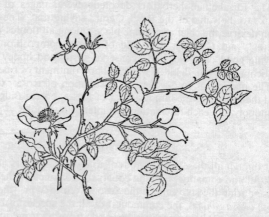

During the 1914–18 War the suggestion was made that British housewives should preserve Rose-hips for jam, as they were so beneficial, but the great difficulty was the complete extraction of the extremely hairy seeds inside the fleshy pulp. Directions were to cut open the fruit and take out the seeds – a long, tedious process, and not always effective. And if some of these stiff, sharply pointed hairs are left in the preserve they irritate the throat and intestines, and are a source of danger, especially to children. It needed the urgency of the Second World War for a real solution to this difficulty in the commercial manufacture of Rose-hip syrup.

Though Vitamin C, that most vital product of Rose hips, was discovered about twenty-five years ago, it was not till research work was carried out from 1934 onwards that it was found that the red berries of the English Rose contained more of this valuable substance than any other fruit or vegetable – four times as much as blackcurrant juice and twenty times as much as oranges.

Vitamin C, the anti-scorbutic vitamin, present in all citrus fruits, prevents scurvy and other diseases due to malnutrition, a fact dimly comprehended by Captain Cook and other navigators when they insisted that lemons should be included in seamen's diet on long voyages in sailing-ships. Though scurvy, as such, has practically vanished, owing to the nation's large consumption of green vegetables, an ample sufficiency of Vitamin C in our food also helps to promote healthy growth of tissue, bones and teeth, and assists in the production of the red cells of the blood, thus preventing anaemia.

Experiments made during the war with fracture cases have definitely proved that patients who received Rose-hip syrup progressed more rapidly than those who did not. Rose-hips also contain Vitamins A and P, still rather unknown factors, into which investigation is still being carried on.

THE NATION'S CONTRIBUTION

When total war threw Britain on her own resources, stopping the imports of citrus fruit and reducing the acreage of blackcurrants and other soft fruit to permit a huge increase in arable land, the various Ministries dealing with the country's food saw that only a nation-wide collection of Rose-hips could increase the nation's supply of Vitamin C.

The Ministry of Health in 1941 put forward a scheme for Rose-hip collection, and 120 tons were gathered that year by voluntary collectors. The following year the scheme was transferred to the Vegetable Drugs Committee of the Ministry of Supply, and this committee, with collectors, chemists and drug firms, drew up 'Operation Rose', with a resulting amount of 344 tons. In 1943, when every Herb Committee in each county organised its forces, and with favourable weather during July and August, the amount increased to 500 tons. But the wet summer of 1944, as well as aerial warfare, reduced the tonnage to 400. With the ending of the war in 1945, county committees concentrated almost entirely on Rose-hips and 480 tons were gathered.

The Vegetable Drugs Committee of the Ministry of Supply closed down in 1946, leaving County Herb Committees to make their own decisions as to carrying on with collection. As the food situation had worsened owing to conditions in Europe, many committees felt that a further effort was needed of them.

MORE VITAMIN C IN THE NORTH

Apart from the economic value of the Rose-hip collections, many interesting facts were discovered by scientists during the war years with regard to this little-known fruit. Perhaps the main point emerging is that Vitamin C is a variable factor according to geographical position and variety of the plants. For instance, Rose-hips growing in Scotland are in some cases ten times as valuable as those grown in Cornwall, and one kind, identified by Russian botanists as *Rosa cinnamomea*, contains nearly 5 per cent of the vitamin, while *Rosa canina*, growing in Hertfordshire, has yielded only 0·4 per cent. It is now generally accepted that the more northerly parts of Europe appear to produce Rose-hips containing the greatest amount of ascorbic acid.

Though it is sometimes said that there are only five species of Wild Rose, the plants have hybridised to such an extent that many sub-species or variations are now in existence, each producing Vitamin C of variable amount. *Rosa mollis*, the Soft-leaved Rose, with deep-pink flowers, is found almost exclusively in the north of England and in Scotland, and is very much richer in the vitamin than the Field Rose (*Rosa arvensis*), with white flowers and a trailing habit of growth, found mainly in the south of these islands, while the Burnet Rose (*Rosa spinosissima*), with cream flowers and purplish-black berries, is very deficient in it. *Rosa canina*, the Dog Rose, common all over the British Isles, varies in its vitamin content according to its geographical source.

COMMERCIAL PRODUCTION

As has already been mentioned, some people, hearing of the benefit to health of Rose-hips, have in recent years attempted to preserve the berries. But certain difficulties have usually arisen in manufacture – the extraction of the hairs and the fact that, owing to long-continued cooking, the resulting confection may not contain any appreciable amount of Vitamin C, as this element is very elusive and easily destroyed.

Long and searching experiments were carried out when the decision was taken to produce Rose-hip Syrup for the public, so that the highest amount of ascorbic acid might be retained in the finished product. New plant was prepared in up-to-date factories, and the whole process was under strict scientific control. One of the greatest difficulties during the war years, when transport was mainly reserved for priority freights, was to make sure the hips were received at the works as speedily as possible. Collectors were asked to send only sound fruit, under- rather than over-ripe, and to dispatch it carefully labelled in sacks direct to the factories.

The process then was as follows, according to details kindly supplied by the Rose-hips Products Association: –

'The hips are either processed as soon as possible after picking or frozen solid at a low temperature to preserve the vitamin. The refrigerated hips or the fresh hips are then coarsely ground and treated very rapidly with boiling water to destroy an enzyme present in the hips which inactivates Vitamin C extremely rapidly. While the hips remain whole or frozen the enzyme is unable to attack the Vitamin C; after crushing, unless protective measures are taken to destroy the enzyme, the whole of the Vitamin C can be easily lost. Hot-water extraction is performed in various ways, the main being by percolation of hot water through a bed of crushed hips, or alternatively by maceration, in which the crushed hips, in linen bags, are suspended in boiling water. The watery extract is tested for Vitamin C, concentrated under reduced pressure at a low temperature to preserve the vitamin, and the requisite quantity of sugar added to produce a syrup falling within the limits agreed by the Ministry of Health. The vitamin content is again determined analytically, to ensure that when the syrup leaves the maker it contains no less than the minimum requirement of 200 milligrams per 100 millilitres of syrup.'

When the various processes are completed, the syrup is quickly bottled and sealed, and is then ready for dispatch to retailers.

In Denmark, Norway and Russia, and to some extent in Great Britain, tablets have been made from Rose-hips. The extract is concentrated and dried *in vacuo*, and the resultant mixture is then compressed into tablets. These are more stable than the syrup, keeping indefinitely.

During the war, National Rose-hip Syrup was sold at a controlled price of 1s. 9d. a six-ounce bottle through ordinary trade channels, Welfare Clinics being able to buy it in larger containers. Mothers and children, and the general public, were then able to obtain it through several sources, to help to make up deficiency of Vitamin C caused by limitations of rationed foods and shortages of imported and home-grown fruits.

For, though the average human adult requires daily only 25–30 milligrams of ascorbic acid as a minimum, a child needs 100–150 milligrams, but during pregnancy, lactation, in illness and old age the requirements of an adult are very considerably increased. Though no scientific proof is yet available, rheumatic sufferers have repeatedly stated that Rose-hip Syrup has been of great benefit to them.

But the disquieting fact remains that though every year the hedges are laden with these precious fruits, the supply of Rose-hip Syrup has never been equal to the demand. And if enough is to be available for all our own people who require it, with some left over for the ill-nourished children of Europe, a great many more collectors are necessary.

During 1945, after the war had ended, enquiries were made in Europe as to the extent of the use of Rose-hips. Information was difficult to obtain, but the Soviet Union reported that the women and the children of the Tatar Republic had collected large amounts of the fruit, the High School pupils alone having in one season delivered 17 tons of dried berries. The old Tatars in this little Republic have long called Rose-hips 'the fruit of life'.

GARDEN OR CULINARY HERBS

There is no hard-and-fast line between medicinal and garden herbs, for some of the wild plants used in medicine are useful also in food and flavouring, while most of the garden or culinary herbs have a greater or less value in medicine.

Even the name 'sweet herbs', often given to the garden varieties, is not quite correct, for no one who has ever tasted Rue or Rosemary or Southernwood could call them sweet. In fact, the last-named plant, which is actually one of the Wormwoods, has so unpleasantly bitter a taste that even bees and butterflies avoid it, and it is called '*Garderobe*' by the French owing to its power in keeping away moths from clothes cupboards.

Perhaps the best method of definition is that nearly all 'garden herbs' are cultivated ones, and, except as occasional escapes, do not grow wild in field or meadow. A large number of them are not indigenous (native), for many came long years ago from the Mediterranean shores, where they have flourished under sunny skies from time immemorial.

Herbs have throughout the ages been brought into the British Isles by various means. The Romans, in the positive manner of all military conquerors, believed *Britannia* was to be one of their colonies for all time, and brought seeds and plants of many of their favourite herbs for the benefit of their own people, no doubt cultivating them around their camps and villas, and making gay and fragrant gardens during their 400 years of occupation of these islands, for the Romans, like the modern Italians, were keen gardeners.

Other means of introduction have been from imported grain, through foreign seed used for cage-birds, by fertilisers brought from far-off countries, and, in later days, by ballast in ships, and recently by sandbags employed in anti-blast defences.

After the Romans left these islands, monastic gardens carried on the cultivation of garden herbs, and in mediaeval times, when there was no effective means of storing meat and game, strongly flavoured herbs lavishly used were the only means at hand to disguise the very evident decay.

One has only to read recipes in old cookery books to notice how abundantly herbs of all kinds were used in the pies and possets of the enormous meals the wealthier families indulged in several times a day. Cocktails as appetisers being then unknown, strongly flavoured herbs were eaten to stimulate the appetite, as well as to conceal rank flavours, and not least to aid digestion.

The entire lack of sanitation, the filth of houses and streets, the unsavoury condition of prisons and courts and the uncleanliness of the mass of the people made some sort of sweet-smelling antidote imperative, and thus arose the pomander carried by the wealthy from the time of the ancient Greeks.

The pomander, derived from '*pomme*' and '*amber*', because of its rounded shape like an apple, and because it originally included ambergris as one of its ingredients, survived in some form throughout the years, finally resulting in the vinaigrette of the last century. In Pliny's time, early in the Christian era, herbs and spices were pounded with wine or honey, and enclosed in a golden globe pierced with holes to allow the scent to escape. Cardinal Wolsey is often pictured with an orange, the peel of the fruit filled with sweet-smelling herbs; in the Middle Ages a favourite mixture was composed of Cedar-wood, Orange and Lemon peel, Rose leaves, Sweet Sedge, Cloves, Orris root (the root of the Florentine Iris), Rosemary and Rue, Musk, oil of Lily-of-the-valley mashed to a pulp with Rose-water and inserted into a metal container. The same idea was found in the 'sleeping apple' mentioned by Bacon, where a ball of some porous material was filled with crushed Hemlock, Mandrake, Poppy, Henbane and Lettuce, placed on the pillow to induce sleep. To our minds, it would be much more likely to produce nightmare!

The custom of strewing houses and public places with odorous herbs was followed not merely because of the fragrance they exuded when trodden, but so that they should act as a disinfectant during outbreaks of plague and other highly infectious diseases. Herbs are mildly antiseptic, and afforded some degree of amelioration of the foul stench of plague-pits, of unwashed prisoners and the sickly smell of the open, festering sores that seem to have beset many of the people in the 'bad old times'.

A much more pleasant side to the use of sweet herbs was in the making of scents, perfumes, pot-pourri, sachets, cosmetics, as well as all kinds of confectionery, sweetmeats, syrups, creams, not forgetting those very important – and generally impotent – mixtures known as love-potions and love-philtres.

Though many of the perfumes were composed mainly of such flowers as Violet, Rose and Jasmin, quite a number contained fragrant herbs; for instance, one famous seventeenth-century recipe invented by an Englishman and used by, among others, George IV, had as its three main ingredients Bergamot, Red Rose and Florentine Iris. Eastern spices and resins were largely used in perfumes, but such penetrating odours as Lavender, Bergamot and Musk were freely mingled among them, and one very delightful 'tincture of lavender' was made up of Saffron, Cowslips, Borage, Lavender, Rosemary, Lilies-of-the-valley, Bergamot and other herbs.

During the leisurely days of the Tudors and Stuarts, when physicians and shops in the villages were few and far between, the lady at the Hall was mistress of the still-room, where she compounded medicines for her family and servants, dried and stored herbs, conserved fruit, concocted perfumes and powders, distilled oils and tinctures, and devised elaborate syrups and confections from the herbs and flowers growing so luxuriantly in the garden.

For every house, large or small, owned either a herb-garden or a herb border, and still to-day in some old gardens one finds traces of 'Tudor gardens' edged with box, 'Gardens of Fragrance', and other delightful relics. For the most part, however, these gardens have vanished, and their place has been taken by ornamental or formal or Italian or Rose-gardens, and, latest fashion of all, the rock or alpine garden.

HERB CULTIVATION

With the development of town life during the eighteenth and nineteenth centuries, market-gardeners took up the cultivation of herbs, both for drugs, culinary use, and perfumes, especially around London; Mitcham, for instance, became the centre of Lavender-growing. But by the end of the nineteenth century herb cultivation had considerably declined. The reasons for this were, partly the ever-increasing imports from Europe, and partly the development of synthetic substances which were substituted in medicines and scents.

Although a great deal was done in the cultivation of herbs and the planning of herb-gardens and small herb-farms during and after the 1914–18 War, interest in them again began to flag, and the small prices offered to herb-growers by druggists drove many of the small commercial farms out of existence. By the time another World War broke out, the cultivation of herbs had sunk to a rather low level. In most gardens only four kinds of herb – Mint, Sage, Parsley and Thyme – survived, scattered in any odd corner, far from the kitchen, and consisting often of old, woody plants, bearing small, flavourless leaves and infested with weeds.

The cessation of imports of those convenient little packages of dried culinary herbs from France, Belgium and Germany gave a decided jolt to housewives, and inquiries began to be made as to the cultivation of these sweet herbs, and, with the help of herb specialists, the Ministry of Agriculture and secretaries of County Herb Committees, the old enthusiasm for savoury herbs was gradually revived. Many herb-gardens were started, or at least plants were collected into a border and made accessible to the kitchen. As Europe had sent us a large proportion of all the dried herbs consumed in these islands, there was a great gap to be filled, and vigorous work, both educational and physical, had to be undertaken to make good the loss.

The Ministry of Agriculture in 1942 published an excellent Bulletin (No. 125, *Culinary Herbs and their Cultivation*), herb exhibitions and lectures stimulated effort, and housewives once again grew and dried and stored those precious flavourings which they had so greatly missed. Not only did individual gardeners start growing herbs, but local educational authorities encouraged horticultural teachers to give more space to herbs in their instructional gardens, and recently the National Farmers' Union, at the request of some of its members, has advised its horticultural specialists to take up the matter of commercial herb-growing with the druggists and herb merchants.

Even though small quantities of sweet herbs are now being imported from European Countries, there is every reason for anyone with a garden to devote some space in it to the cultivation of at least the five sweet herbs forming that delicious bouquet of mixed herbs: Mint, Sage, Parsley, Thyme and Marjoram. Herbs grown in one's own garden are likely to be much superior in flavour to the packed article from other countries, and those gathered fresh, like home-grown vegetables, have a higher nutritive value than the dried article. It has been stated that fresh Parsley contains a greater percentage of iron than almost any other vegetable.

People with large gardens might very profitably allow space for a herb-garden, the planning and arranging of which are dealt with in a special section, but general principles of gathering, drying and marketing may be considered here.

126

The large majority of plants are needed for the 'herb' – that is, the whole plant cut just above the root. From others only the leaves are required, while a number, such as Dill, Caraway and Coriander, are produced for their fruit, or 'seed'; with others the flower petals are their chief product, as with Marigold, *Rosa gallica* or Lavender; Angelica and Lovage supply us with their juicy, sweet-flavoured stems for confectionery and preserves, and with a small proportion it is the bulb that is required, while a few have the roots as drug or delight.

As far as possible, herbs should be eaten in the fresh state, for they impart a finer and more intense flavour to soups and stews than does the dried article. Naturally, from the point of view of colour, only fresh herbs can be used in salads.

But various dried herbs are an essential part of the store cupboard, and every housewife will wish to make the drying and storing of herbs from her garden a regular part of her summer preserving plans. All the suggestions here given apply as much to drug plants as to the culinary varieties.

COLLECTING HERBS

Gathering herbs is a delightful task, for it is done at the best time of the day – after the dew has left the plants, and before the sun becomes too hot. The plants should just be opening into blossom, for the aromatic flavour and essential oil of herbs are at their maximum when leaves and blossoms are at their best. A day without rain which has been sunny since daybreak is ideal for collecting, as, though some leaves may dry quickly after rain, others, like the thick, furry ones of Horehound or Mint, retain the moisture, and if allowed to be massed before drying may easily develop mould and become spoilt. Too much heat, on the other hand, dries up the oil in the leaves. Only the best-shaped, greenest leaves should be gathered, and any that are withered, insect-bitten or stained should be discarded. This applies also when the whole plant is gathered, for the leaves nearest the root may be imperfect.

As far as possible, grass and other extraneous matter should be cleaned out while the plants are being gathered. This saves quite a lot of time when preparing the plants for the drying-racks. If the leaves of many different plants are to be plucked at one gathering, different containers should be used. Sorting out the tiny leaves of Thyme, for example, from other herbs is a long and tiresome job. Only as much herb as can be dried without crowding in the drying-places should be collected, for if leaves are crammed together when drying, a great many may damp off and be wasted.

Leaves and herbs should be cut with a sharp knife or secateurs, for pulling them off by hand may easily damage the tender stems of plants, causing delay in new growth or the entry of fungus or insects into the damaged tissues.

DRYING HERBS

Unfortunately from the collectors' point of view, most herbs are ready to be gathered at the same time of the year, so plenty of drying space should be made ready from May onwards.

Drying herbs is quite a simple matter, though care and daily attention are necessary. Those with woody stems should be tied loosely, about a dozen in a bunch, and, if the weather is really warm, they may be hung out-of-doors in half-shade against a brick wall, fence or trellis. At some schools during the war the children laid the plants out singly on sheets of paper on the tarmac playground, with very good results. But bunches or plants must be taken indoors long before evening, as the damp rises from the ground, and by leaving them out all the day's work will be lost.

The main idea in drying is that the herbs should not lose their colour, for not only does this spoil the appearance of the dried article, but it also means a loss of oil and fragrance. To achieve this, leaves must be dried as quickly as possible, and not with too intense a heat.

One of the handiest places for drying small amounts is in a warm kitchen, where bunches may be hung up on strings fairly near the ceiling, though not so high as to make the turning of them a constant labour, or so low that they catch on the heads of people going in and out! Those with succulent stems may be spread thinly on paper on the rack of the stove, or, better still, so that cooking arrangements do not interfere with the drying, wire or canvas or butter-muslin frames on supports can be placed above the rack. Bunches of herbs should be covered in paper or muslin bags and those spread on racks should also be protected from flies and insects.

Other places for drying bunches of herbs are a warm shed or garage, attics, lofts and spare rooms, or a cool greenhouse, provided the plants are protected with paper from too fierce a mid-day heat and given sufficient ventilation.

If there is a great deal of drying to be done, it is not a difficult matter to fix up a dark outdoor shed as a drying-house. Strings can be stretched from side to side fairly near the roof, tied to cup-hooks or nails in the walls, and will take many bunches of herbs. Wire-mesh trays piled up one above the other, or wire racks built up into a framework, like apple-drying trays, can be stacked around the walls, taking care that they are easily accessible so that shaking and turning the herbs is easy, and that there is plenty of air-space. If racks are not possible, canvas or muslin 'hammocks' may be stretched across the shed from hooks fastened in the walls.

But wherever and however drying is done, time must be spared every day for turning the bunches, so that the central stalks dry as quickly as the outside ones, and for shaking and inspecting all the trays of leaves. Oven-drying, though sometimes advocated, is not desirable. It is difficult to estimate the temperature of the oven, emergency cooking may cause the herbs to be bundled out of the way, and too great heat will certainly cause evaporation of oils, and thus disperse the bright-green colour. During the war, some herb-gatherers had access to bakers' ovens after baking was finished, or to drying-kilns.

When the bunched herbs appear to be nearly dry, leaves can be stripped, laid out on racks and dried until they are crisp and ready to be powdered.

The drying of flowers has to be done with even greater care than that of the leaves, and an excellent place for this, especially if the delicate blooms are required for pot-pourri, is the hot-air cupboard. Blossoms should be spread singly on racks covered with muslin or fine wire, on fine-meshed cake-racks, or in cardboard or paper boxes lined with thin paper, placed one above the other, and stacked in the warm, dark cupboard. If the cupboard becomes too hot, the door may be left ajar. In a week or ten days even the frail flowers of Jasmine, Rose, Borage, Lavender, Rosemary and other bright blooms should be well and colourfully dried.

Fortunately for the busy herb-grower, seed is harvested later than most of the leafy herbs, but as the time of ripening varies with the state of the weather, careful watch must be kept on the plants, as the birds may steal the seeds or the capsules burst open and scatter their contents broadcast. Dill, Caraway, Coriander and Chervil are so valuable either in the kitchen or in medicine, and are so easy to grow, that at least a few clumps of each should find a place in the herb-garden. As long as the seed-heads are cut at the right moment and put to dry, there is not the same urgent haste as with leaves and flowers, and threshing or cleaning can be delayed for evenings or some more leisured moments.

Great care must be taken with seed-heads to keep each variety separate and to label trays or bunches with the correct name, as they are somewhat similar in appearance, especially in the dried state. In small quantities, seed may be roughly cleaned from the stalks by hand, taking out the larger impurities – stem, chaff, etc. But to get the perfect specimen – and only such will be accepted by herb merchants – the seed must be sieved and carefully picked over. Drying the seed takes about a week or a fortnight, according to weather and the size of different seeds, but a strict watch must be kept if they are dried outdoors in a shed, as mice are very fond of these oily fruits.

NEXT YEAR'S SEED

Not only those herbs specially grown for seed, but a few choice plants of most herbs should be allowed to fruit, thus ensuring a supply of good fresh seed for next year's planting. Surplus seed can always be given to other enthusiasts, or, in times of scarcity, be sold to nurserymen and druggists. An example of unexpected seed shortage was experienced in 1942, when practically no caraway seed was obtainable in the British Isles, and the Government offered to buy any quantity of it, even from small growers. This shows how very dependent we have been on foreign supplies, for this easily-grown plant was once a staple crop in Essex.

DRYING ROOTS

Roots are perhaps the most difficult part of herbs to dry, especially as they are usually in a very damp condition when dug, since digging takes place in the autumn, when the soil is likely to be muddy and sticky. Roots must not be dug for medicine while the leaves are still in full growth, as they have not achieved their maximum medicinal content, some of this still being retained in the part of the plant above ground.

When lifting, an effort must be made to get out the entire root, so a long spade or fork is needed. The roots will come up with pieces of mud and other particles adhering to them, probably as well as other verdure, such as grass. A good deal of this can be scraped off, but the only really efficient way to clean roots is by thorough washing, and scrubbing is usually necessary. Top stems and rootlets should then be cut off, and large roots, such as those of Liquorice and Burdock, may be sliced to hasten drying.

To dry, they should be spread out, without touching, on shelves, or tied singly on string in a warm shed or greenhouse for about ten days, being turned and inspected every day. When they have started to shrink well (roots lose about three-quarters of their weight in drying) they can be finished off in heat over a stove or in a cool oven. This will probably take another ten days, but is dependent on the moisture in the atmosphere. Roots are dry when they are quite brittle.

Bulbs and corms are tied up in small bunches, like onions, in a shed, constant watch being kept to see that they are drying evenly.

ARTIFICIAL HEATING

During a normally hot summer the majority of herbs can be dried indoors in a warm building or room without artificial heat. But if some sort of artificial heat can be provided, the herbs will dry more quickly and evenly, wet or damp weather can be ignored, all the herbs can be dried under the one roof, thus saving time and labour, and the more difficult leaves, such as those of Foxglove and Mullein, and flowers like Elderberry, can be satisfactorily finished with much less trouble.

The ideal method of heating is the greenhouse stove with pipes so that the heat is evenly distributed. But this is an impossibility in most cases, and a substitute has to be improvised. A slow-combustion stove or a 'tortoise' gives an even heat and does not require much stoking, while one or two oil-stoves are quite adequate during the summer. One oil-stove of the kind known as the 'cathedral stove', often used in churches, is excellent.

As the temperature should be between 90 and 100 degrees, if possible, the stoves must be kept going continuously, and those plants which need the greatest heat, such as Comfrey, Belladonna and Parsley, should be arranged nearest to the heating apparatus.

Another great advantage of a heated building is that herbs which have for one reason or another to be stored before dispatch, can be kept without fear of damage, provided they are inspected regularly and the sacks or boxes in which they are packed shaken from time to time. Sacks and boxes of dried herbs should on no account be stood on a brick or stone floor; wood or thick cardboard should be placed beneath them or they should be hung up.

STORING

Most of the medicinal herbs will be sent off to the druggists, but small quantities of some of them, and certainly a good amount of the sweet herbs, will have to be stored, and the drying-shed, when freed of the summer's bulky greenery, will probably accommodate all those required for home use or for small winter sales.

Those herbs needed for winter use, involving rather lengthy storing, should be packed into glass jars with airtight covers, or into paper-lined tins, and arranged in a dark place, for if exposed to light, they will quickly lose their colour. Paper or cardboard packets are not desirable, as the oil, being volatile, will soak into a porous material. If herbs are to be marketed at a Women's Institute shop or elsewhere for a speedy sale, cellulose bags may be used. Roots are stored in the same way, but flowers are best made up at once into sachets or bags or pot-pourri, or sent off to druggists for distillation. If sent away by post, they can be packed in small, paper-lined boxes, or those handy little cereal and flour bags now obtainable from grocers.

MARKETING

A good many people will ask: 'Now, having grown and dried and stored my herbs, what can I do with them?' This, of course, depends on the individual grower. If herb-growing is to be undertaken for the commercial market, it is imperative first to find out several points from various drug firms: what plants they specially require, the minimum amounts they will take in one lot, what prices are paid, and during what months of the year the herbs are required, and if they have a closing date for accepting herbs.

Druggists are business men, and must be dealt with in a business-like way. The prices paid for dried herbs are small, and only by a proper selection, quick and efficient drying and despatch, can any kind of profit be made. Some herb-growers may wish to set up a mail-order business of their own for herb-plants and dried goods, but they must be prepared for long, arduous and continuous work.

For some time to come, we are told, there will be a shortage of garden herbs in grocers' and other shops, and well-dried, daintily packed herbs will have a ready sale. The Women's Institute Market shops and stalls, now spread all over the country, have also a steady demand for dried herbs from their customers.

But the majority of people who grow herbs in their own small plots will find a constant use for them in their own and their friends' kitchens. Sweet and savoury dishes, poultry, salads, sandwiches are very much improved by a flavouring of herbs – in fact, there is scarcely any dish to which one or more of the sweet herbs described in this book cannot be beneficially added.

USE FOR HERBS

English people often comment on the delicious, uncommon flavour of meat and cooked dishes and confectionery made by French, Belgian, Dutch and other European cooks. The reason for this savour is usually a careful and considered use of various herbs. In the United States, too, herbs have again come into favour and many a housewife uses those seasoning plants, often the descendants of herbs lovingly carried across the wide seas from this country by the Pilgrim Fathers – and Mothers. Herb-trays – dishes divided up into compartments rather like hors d'œuvre dishes – are served at meals, each compartment filled with chopped herbs of various kinds to be sprinkled over food as it is set upon the table. It is an idea we in Britain might well adopt.

'BETTER A DINNER OF HERBS'

This section is for housewives, to show in a practical way how they can serve up the herbs grown in their gardens for an everyday meal.

This menu is being compiled in the lean days of 1946, when ingredients are rather restricted, but when years of plenty come again all kinds of variations will suggest themselves to 'our cunning Cookes'. But these dishes are available at all times – and don't they make your mouth water!

> Artichoke (or Potato or Tomato) Soup aux fines herbes
> Baked Fish with Fennel Sauce
> Tomato Cups, Savoury Potatoes
> Jam Tart, with Rhubarb and Angelica Jam
> Herb Cheese
> Oatmeal Biscuits
> Dandelion Coffee

Artichoke Soup aux fines herbes

These vegetables are delicious, but most exasperating to peel. The easiest method is to boil them gently first and peel afterwards. Drop into cold, salted water as soon as peeled, or they will discolour. Grate or chop finely an onion or several shallots, add this with the sliced artichokes to a pint of white stock, or milk, or milk and water, salt and pepper (celery salt if you have it), ½ oz. of fat, and simmer for half an hour or until the artichokes have pulped down. Mash through a sieve, boil again, and just before serving stir in a large teaspoonful of chopped chives, mint and parsley.

Fish with Fennel Sauce

'Fish boiled is fish spoiled', so whatever kind of fish is available, bake in the oven with a piece of fat, two tablespoonfuls of water, pepper and salt dusted over, covering with a piece of paper. Cook slowly, making the sauce meanwhile. (Fennel is excellent with the more oily fish, salmon, mackerel or fresh herrings.)

Make a white sauce in the usual way, using any liquid left over from the fish, chop a few fennel leaves very small, add to the sauce and serve very hot in a sauce boat. Arrange sprigs of fennel around the dish on which the fish is served.

Tomato Cups

Almost everyone now grows his own tomatoes, so this dish is quite a simple one to procure – provided your herb-border is well stocked. Choose large tomatoes, carefully scoop out the pulp, mix it with chopped chives, mint, one or two nasturtium leaves, carrot, chervil, salt and pepper and put back in the tomatoes. Bake gently. A topping with mayonnaise or thick horseradish sauce will give that additional sharp flavour so beloved by most people. Serve on a dish with sprigs of watercress.

Savoury Potatoes

New potatoes or small old ones boiled in their skins, peeled, and served in an oven-glass dish are greatly improved by a sprinkling of parsley and a pinch or two of tarragon and thyme.

Jam Tart with Angelica Jam

The stout, juicy, fragrant stalks of young angelica can be added to several fruits to make jam, but are a perfect combination with the rather insipid rhubarb. Cut the angelica stalks into small pieces and add about one-eighth part to every part of rhubarb. People either like angelica or they don't, so be rather sparing of this herb until you know just how much your family can stand. Increase the amount of angelica with discretion. Add sugar and boil up as for other preserves.

Make a pastry lining for the tart in the usual way, and fill with the angelica jam.

Oatmeal Biscuits

These, made with 2 oz. of flour, 2 oz. of medium oatmeal, mixed to a stiff paste with 1 oz. – or more – of melted fat and a little water, cut into rounds and baked until light brown, go very well with a soft cheese into which a little finely chopped sage has been worked with a silver knife.

Dandelion Coffee

This is made from dandelion roots that have been dried and roasted in the oven, then crushed into powder.

SALADS

Salads can take so many forms and can be varied in such diverse ways that only suggestions can be made here. For the basis of the salad nothing really compares with crisp, green lettuce leaves, and over these many kinds of vegetables and herbs can be arranged. When tomatoes and beet can be procured, these add colour and flavour, though the beet must be thinly sliced and used with care. Finely cut, tender cabbage or brussels sprouts and grated carrot are other pleasant ingredients, and celery chopped finely gives crispness and a distinctive taste. Cooked young green peas add food value, asparagus tops an air of luxury, cucumber (unpeeled) is liked by some people, and nasturtium seeds (chopped, and in moderation) are a really good relish. Hard-boiled eggs, though beloved of British salad-makers, should be used only with certain salads, and, naturally, not with a Green Salad.

Whatever the mixture of vegetables, green herbs may always be added, but care is necessary in the amount of each herb, and they should be well blended with the other ingredients so that no one flavour is predominant. Many of the sweet herbs may be used, but the novice in herb salads would be well advised to start with mint, parsley, thyme, marjoram and chives.

Herbs strange to most salad-makers, but well worth trying, are tarragon, chervil, balm, fennel, basil, salad burnet, savory, as well as the young petals of nasturtium, marigold, red rose and borage, giving a delightful colour effect. To obtain the full flavour of a herb salad, mayonnaise should not be eaten with it. A French dressing – for preference, and if obtainable – is a judicious mixture of salad oil and lemon juice.

OTHER HERB RECIPES

MINT JELLY, sold in normal times at quite extravagant prices, is cheap and simple to make at home, and when sugar is again plentiful every housewife should include this pungent preserve to add to those always made for the store cupboard. Mint may be either spearmint or apple-mint, the latter giving the better flavour, perhaps, and only fresh young leaves should be chosen. The quantity of mint depends rather on the amount of minty flavour required, but six stalks to 6 lb. of apples is usually sufficient.

The apples should be of the green acid varieties, cut into slices and put into a pan with the mint-stalks tied together and just enough water to cover. Bring to boiling point and simmer until the fruit is well pulped. Allow to drain through a flannel bag for at least twelve hours. The following day measure the liquid and allow 1 lb. of sugar to 1 pint of juice, bring to the boil again quickly, immersing a bunch of young mint leaves. At this point it is just as well to taste the jelly, and if the flavour is strong enough, whisk out the mint and simmer until setting point is reached. Usually a few drops of vegetable colouring are needed to give that luscious deep-green tint so much admired in all shop jelly. Pot in the usual way. It is a fascinating addition to lamb or mutton, or indeed to any savoury dish.

PEPPERMINT JELLY – a delicious medicine for sore throats – can be made in a similar way to mint jelly, but, as this herb is somewhat strongly flavoured, some experimenting is required to obtain the correct flavour.

APPLE OR ELDERFLOWER JELLY may be varied by the addition of lavender flowers.

An American 'dessert' is VIOLET JELLY. Here is how to make it, if you like experiments. Gather about 1 oz. of fresh young violet blossoms, pluck off stalks and calices, wash and drain off all moisture. Make a syrup of one pint of water and 1 lb. of sugar, and add the violets, stirring gently and bringing the liquid to the boil. Simmer gently for about twenty minutes. Strain through muslin and allow to cool. Add 1 oz. of powdered gelatine to each pint of syrup and heat, but on no account allow the liquid to boil. Pour into a mould which has been rinsed in cold water, and when turned out arrange violets round it. The addition of a few drops of violet colouring may be needed to achieve the correct tint. Rose-petals may be used in the same way.

TARRAGON VINEGAR is the only herb vinegar of the many beloved by our grandmothers which has survived. But many garden herbs may be made into tasteful vinegars, including chervil, marjoram, mint, savory – and here is the recipe. Crush well-washed young fresh leaves of the herb into a wide-mouthed jar, fill with white vinegar, tightly cork, stand in a warm place, shaking every day for about a week, strain through muslin into a pickle or sauce bottle and fasten securely.

One last recipe – POT-POURRI – must be added. Almost any kind of flowers may be chosen, chiefly for their scent and bright colour. The gathering of the blossoms should take place during a spell of warm weather, about mid-morning. Buds just opening retain their fragrance and hue the longest. Arrange the blooms on trays in the hot-air cupboard as suggested under flower-drying, and leave for about ten days. When dry, they should still have all their original sweet-scented vividness. A little powdered orris root may be added, if desired. This is the simplest form of pot-pourri; but all kinds of variations with leaves, oils and flowers can be carried out.

HERB DESCRIPTIONS

ANGELICA
Archangelica officinalis, Umbelliferae

It is very good to know that the delicious, rather expensive, Angelica of confectionery will not only grow, but thrive and become a tall, handsome plant in the gardens of the British Isles. No doubt most of the crystallised Angelica that was once bought for festive iced cakes came from European countries, but it could quite easily have been grown and candied at home.

It is a native of the northerly parts of Russia, Lithuania and Germany, but was brought to Britain during the sixteenth century and has been cultivated ever since. Gerard and the other herbalists grew it. Parkinson writes of it as 'a herbe of most especiall use' and herb-farms around London found its cultivation profitable. Beautiful specimens of it can now be seen in the Chelsea Physic Garden and at the Royal Botanic Gardens at Kew.

Angelica is almost a perennial, but the old plants die off after seeding, and young plants take about a year before they make much growth, usually to die out in the second or third year. It bears large seed-heads, which scatter seeds when ripe, producing new plants. A rather damp, shady position is the most suitable, and it is quite unaffected by frost and snow. It grows quite well from seed, though shoots of a two-year-old plant are a quicker method of reproduction.

Angelica is a tall, showy plant with large, much-divided, bright green leaves and broad umbels of white flowers. The stems are thick and hollow, and have a delightful aromatic scent, which is preserved in the candied product. The name 'archangel' may come either from its association with northern Russia, or from the legend that it is supposed to flower at about St Michael the Archangel's Day. Old tales connect it with angelic powers against evil spirits, spells and witchcraft.

At the present time its benefits are much more practical, as leaves, root and seed are all used medicinally. These possess stimulant and tonic properties, are valued in digestive troubles, for producing perspiration and clearing up coughs, colds and bronchial ailments. The stalks slowly chewed in the mouth will relieve flatulence. Its peculiar sweet flavour is useful for neutral-ising the taste of unpleasant-tasting medicine.

In France, where it is largely grown, it has always been a valued ingredient in liqueurs, especially in Chartreuse. The

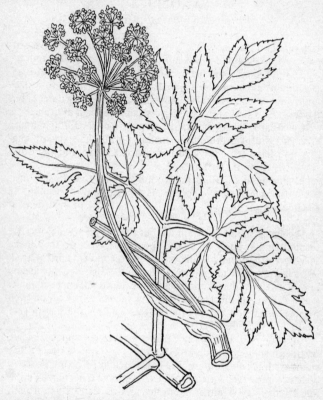

method of crystallising the stems is similar to that employed for such fruits as cherries or violet- and rose-petals. The chopped young stems are added to preserves, especially rhubarb jam, giving a delicious flavour.

Wild Angelica (*Angelica sylvestris*) is not used in medicine, but in some districts the root is candied, though it does not pos-sess the fine flavour of the cultivated variety.

ANISE
Pimpinella anisum, Umbelliferae

This is one of the useful oil-bearing seed plants (included in the large Parsley family which has been employed in medicine and in the kitchen since very early times and has been cultivated here since the sixteenth century. It is a native of the Middle East, and is mentioned in the New Testament, 'for ye pay tithes of mint and anise and cumin'.

Anise is a pretty little plant, with dainty, fern-like leaves and small heads of whitish flowers, and may be sown in April in a warm, sunny border, the seed ripening in about four months. Coming from hot countries, it does not always take very kindly to our damp, chilly climate, but in warm summers it makes good growth and bears a plentiful amount of small, sweet, spicy seed without any of the strong flavour of Caraway or Chervil.

Its value as an aid to digestion is hinted at by the Romans, who, after their rich, sumptuous meals, finished with a cake made of Anise, Cumin and other digestion-aiding seeds. The French strew it over young carrots and add it to salads and soups, while it is quite a delightful addition to apple sauce. On the Continent it is used as an ingredient in cakes, bread and rolls, and also in liqueurs, Anisette being a well-known drink.

Anise is largely used in medicine, for its value in digestive complaints, lozenges as well as liquid drugs being made for this purpose. Aniseed balls were once a favourite form of sweetmeat. The powdered seed is also employed in condition medicine for horses.

BALM
Melissa officinalis, Labiatae

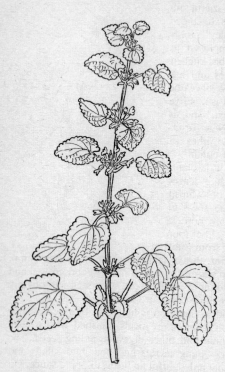

This plant is found growing in almost every garden, often more by accident than design. Bee-keepers sometimes make a plantation of it near the hives, as it has an abundance of nectar stored in the numerous little white flowers. For two thousand years or more Balm has been known and treasured, from the ancient belief that bees will not leave a hive if there is plenty of this plant in the garden; Pliny, the ancient Roman naturalist, affirmed that 'When bees have strayed away, they do find their way home by it'. '*Melissa*', the generic name, is Greek for 'bee', and reference is often made to the plant by Greek authors, for, like many of our sweet herbs, it came originally from the Mediterranean countries.

Balm will grow anywhere, making a little shrubby plant, a foot or so high, with heart-shaped, rough leaves and insignificant blooms. Though it dies down in the winter, it springs up again early in the year, full of vigour and delicious scent. It can be propagated by seed sown in April or May, or by cuttings or root divisions in spring or autumn, not later than October. Apart from keeping the ground around the little plants free from weeds, it needs little attention. The leaves are easily dried by hanging the foliage in small bunches in a warm place, stripping the stalks when dry and lightly powdering the leaves.

Balm was formerly used a great deal more than it is now, and the *London Dispensary* of the seventeenth century says, 'An essence of Balm drunk every morning will renew youth, strengthen the brain, relieve languishing nature, and prevent baldness!'

Although this writer may have somewhat exaggerated the virtues of Balm, it nevertheless has many uses: it makes a cooling drink for feverish patients by reducing the temperature, eases digestive troubles, and is sometimes prescribed for colds and influenza. In early days it was said to bring long life; a Welsh Prince, Llewelyn, reported to have lived to the age of 108 years, being quoted in support of this statement, as he partook of Balm tea every morning and evening.

While lemons were scarce, the dried leaves of Balm were added to marrow jam and apple-jelly, giving a pleasantly distinctive flavour, though certainly not the hard spiciness of lemons. Oil of Balm is employed in the manufacture of perfumes and some forms of pot-pourri are not complete without its sharply acid scent.

BASIL
Ocimum basilicum, Labiatae

Many people know Keats' lovely poem *Isabella and the Pot of Basil*, and Rossetti's poignant picture illustrating the story, but have never seen the plant itself. This is not at all surprising, as it is so little grown in England, being, as Culpeper says, 'a very tender plant'. It must be sown indoors, and not planted out until late May, and will die down at the first touch of frost, for it cannot stand our cold climate. India is its natural home, where it grows luxuriantly, and is revered as sacred to the Hindu gods Vishnu and Krishna. This association with Indian deities may account for its royal name, '*basilicum*', from the Greek word for 'king'.

Two kinds of Basil are grown, Sweet Basil and Bush Basil, the latter not a bush at all, but a little, compact plant, not more than 6 inches tall. Sweet Basil may grow to 2 feet, with a long, straight stalk from which spring spear-shaped, pale-green leaves and tiny white flowers, both possessing a delicious odour. It is now used very little in medicine, but has some value for those suffering from nervous headaches. Its oil is largely employed in perfumery.

English people usually find its taste a little too strong for flavouring, though it is extensively and pleasantly used in France as a pot herb. It can be introduced sparingly into soups and stuffings, just a pinch being quite enough, but we might with great advantage copy that delicacy of the seventeenth century, 'Fetter Lane Sausages', which were said to be famous because of the inclusion of Basil.

BAY LAUREL
Laurus nobilis, Lauraceae

The wreaths which crowned the victors in Greek and Roman games were made of bay, and to-day the chaplets included in the badges of the Royal Air Force are of the same beautiful leaves.

Perhaps we, in these cold islands, have never been able to appreciate the true beauty of the noble Laurel, for here the plant grows only slowly, and though flower-buds are formed, it seldom blooms, and never fruits.

In the Mediterranean countries the Bay becomes a grand tree, 20 to 30 feet in height, with a wealth of creamy-white flowers, later giving place to glossy, purple fruit.

It will grow in almost any soil from cuttings, or preferably suckers, though it thrives best in a light soil and a warm, sheltered position. Through some confusion in names, this graceful historic shrub is apt to be mixed with the Cherry Laurel, an entirely different plant, belonging to the Rose family. This has bright, shiny leaves, valuable for decoration owing to their evergreen qualities, and sometimes glossy scarlet berries are produced. Apart from the difference in appearance, the Cherry Laurel has the invidious distinction of being the source of a virulent poison, yielding prussic acid.

Bay leaves were once always used for flavouring custards and milk puddings, sometimes soups and stews, giving a delightful taste, but, like many other herb ingredients, it is gradually being ousted by synthetic substances. Tinned fish from Russia and sardines from the Mediterranean still contain a bay leaf or two.

The oil, *Oleum laurinum*, from leaves and berries, is used in herbal medicine for rheumatism. The leaves are easily dried for winter use.

BERGAMOT
Monarda didyma, Labiatae

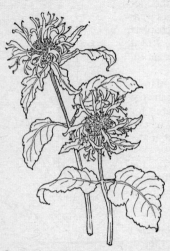

One of the most beautiful and delightful plants for the herb-garden, but, unfortunately, one of the more difficult to grow, is the Crimson Bergamot. Its home is in marshy districts of North America, where it is usually known as 'Oswego Tea', as its young leaves are used to make an infusion, or tea, used both as a drink and for bronchial ailments.

In Britain it is often included in herbaceous borders for the beauty of its rich red flowers, growing in whorls among the large, deep-green leaves, and for its delicious fragrance, unlike any other. It likes a sunny position, but it also needs a deep, moist soil, and one suggestion for ensuring this is to dig into the soil where it is to be planted a generous amount of cow manure. Although it is a perennial, if denied the right situation and treatment it will quickly die out. Where conditions are favourable, it will flourish and grow to a height of 2 to 3 feet, making strong-stemmed, bushy plants. Like other members of the Mint family, it can be propagated by its creeping roots, or by layers or cuttings, although it may be grown from seed sown in April or May.

There are also heliotrope, white and rose varieties, which, though perhaps not quite so vigorous, are just as much sought after by the bees.

It has little medical value, but an infusion of its leaves is sometimes used in country districts for colds and sore throats, as, like all the Mints, it contains thymol, a valuable antiseptic oil. Its main use is in perfumery and for pot-pourri.

BORAGE
Borago officinalis, Boraginaceae

This plant with 'the gallant blew floures' has always been associated with cheerfulness, or as Pliny, long years ago, remarked, 'I, Borage, bring always courage'. Gerard extols its joy-producing properties: 'Those of our time do use the flour in sallads, to exhilerate and make the minde glad. There be also many things made of them, used for the comfort of the heart, to drive away sorrow.

But, whatever its cheering 'vertues' may have been in past years, it is now considered one of the most useful bee-plants, and as leaves and stalks are rich in an alkaline mucilage, it is valued by herbalists for chest and throat complaints. Certainly its appearance is a joy, for it stands boldly upright with its greyish-green leaves and stems covered with fine, white, prickly hairs, and flowers turned back like brilliant blue stars. The whole plant is so ornamental that it was often, as Parkinson says, 'enterposed among women's needleworke'.

It is a useful plant in a herb-garden, as it flowers over a long period, grows in any ordinary soil, will seed freely, coming up year after year in the same place, and can easily be propagated by root division or cuttings. The young leaves can be used in salads, and give a faint cucumber flavour, while the flowers have the same cooling taste, and add greatly to the attractive appearance of this dish. Claret and cider cup and lemonade are improved by the addition of Borage flowers.

CARAWAY
Carum carvi, Umbelliferae

The disappearance of Caraway seed from grocers' shops during the Second World War caused people to think it was a foreign plant. Unfortunately it had almost become one, as practically all Britain's supplies came from Holland and other European countries. Once it was extensively grown in the British Isles, mainly in Essex and Bedfordshire, and supplies were even exported.

Caraway is indigenous in most parts of Europe, and is occasionally found wild in England, though probably a field escape. It is easily grown in clean, light soil, and if sown in the autumn will flower and seed the following year, ripening about July. Seed should be sown in drills, 1 foot apart, and as the plants are small, constant hoeing is needed to keep them clear of weeds. When grown on a large scale, an acre requires about 8 lb. of seed. As soon as the seeds ripen, the plants are cut well above the roots, and harvested at once, as the seed falls very quickly. It is dried in gentle heat.

Everyone knows Caraway cake, but in Holland and Germany, where the plant is grown in large quantities, it is mixed into bread and rolls, and, combined with sugar, makes pleasantly-tasting sweets. Another use is for liqueurs, Kummel having oil of Caraway for its foundation.

In addition to its many culinary uses, it is a valuable medicine, having been used in pharmacy for digestive troubles since very early times; records of its use have been found in an Egyptian papyrus dated 2500 B.C.

Caraway is included in the *British Pharmacopoeia*, and enters into drugs for dyspepsia and for children's ailments, as it is quite pleasant to take. The English Caraway seed is considered the best, on account of its superior flavour. Its combination with other drugs helps to disguise rank tastes and odours.

CHERVIL
Anthriscus cerefolium, Umbelliferae

A delightful herb which ought to be grown much more than it is at present, for its flavour, if used discreetly (as all herbs should be) is pleasant, and it has the further merit of being no trouble either to grow or to dry. In fact, once it has been sown in a garden it is likely to spread everywhere, for its fine seeds are scattered around, and it will germinate at almost any season of the year. But its dainty little green leaves make a lovely lacy carpet, which continues growing quite unconcernedly through snow and frost. Certainly it is a most accommodating plant, with an invigorating odour, and only a few seeds sown broadcast will soon produce a crop of plants.

Its flavour is a little like that of caraway and a little like that of anise, but when used in salads, soups or savoury dishes it blends with other ingredients, imparting a pleasant pungent taste.

Its height is from 2 to 3 feet, and it is not particular as to soil, although it grows more luxuriantly in a sunny position. Being an annual, it should be sown about March in a fairly moist situation. Flowers appear some time in early May, seeding often in June. Later on the stalks and leaves turn mauve, and then tawny red. If leaves only are required for the kitchen, flower-heads should be plucked off as soon as they appear.

Chervil is not now used medicinally, but, as Gerard says, 'the leaves of sweet Chervil are exceedingly good, wholesome and pleasant among other sallad herbs – it exceeds other sallads in wholesomeness for the cold and feeble stomacke'.

CHIVES

Allium schoenoprasum, Amaryllidaceae

Every garden should have a row of Chives, for this plant is very easy to grow and is useful in many different ways. Very occasionally it is found wild in Britain, as are garlic and leeks, but it is really a native of northern Europe and North America. For hundreds of years it has been cultivated in the British Isles, a local name being 'Rushleek' – actually the translation of the somewhat cumbersome specific title.

This plant is a hardy perennial, producing each year fresh leaves from the same bulbs. Someone once called it 'the infant onion', which aptly describes the tiny bulbs from which the plant springs. Chives will grow in any soil, needing a minimum of care – by keeping the old 'grass' (the name often given to the leaves) cut away as it dies, flower-heads plucked and, most important of all, keeping the beds free from weeds. The bulb is shaped like a tiny white shallot, growing in clusters in the same manner. Each little bulb will make a separate plant, and a fine bed of Chives can soon be made from a few roots.

If the Chives are required for their leaves, the flower-heads, of a shape and shade of pink similar to those of Thrift, must be cut off as soon as they appear.

The leaves have a faint onion flavour, and make a delicious addition to salads, omelettes, with mashed potatoes or carrots, in soup and meat dishes, and as they are not so rich in sulphur as onions, they will not cause digestive disturbances. A further merit is that the older and tougher leaves may be chopped and used in poultry mash, especially for chicks and young turkeys.

CLARY
Salvia sclarea, Labiatae

The wild Clary is a native of the British Isles, but the garden variety dates only from the sixteenth century, when it arrived here from southern Europe, and was hailed with delight by the enthusiastic gardeners of that period. Gerard talks of it as growing in Holborn and Chelsea, thus rather suggesting that it was being cultivated in some of the many herb-gardens which flourished at this period, their owners eagerly trying out any of the new seeds or plants they received in such plenty at this time from overseas.

As its name shows, it is one of the Sages, although its scent is milder than that of the Garden Sage; Culpeper says, 'It is of a sweet strong scent'. The plant grows to a height of 2 to 3 feet, with square, brownish stems, large, rough, green leaves, small corollas with brightly coloured bracts – pink, mauve and white varieties are grown. Although really a biennial, it does not always survive the winter, so it is best grown from seed each year. A beautiful variety is Vatican Sage, with large heliotrope flower-heads, growing often to 5 feet tall. It is said to have been originally grown in the gardens of the Vatican. 'Jerusalem Sage', a large greyish-green plant with yellow flowers, is not a culinary herb, and is only placed in borders for ornamental use.

Clary is mostly grown for its oil, highly aromatic, used as a fixer of perfumes. Medicinally, it has been employed for digestive troubles. Once it was considered valuable for the eyes, Culpeper suggesting 'its name is more properly Clear Eye'. Gerard names it '*Oculus Christi*'. John Josselyn, the American herbalist, in the seventeenth century mentions it in the list of herbs introduced into his Boston garden, regretfully recording 'Clary never lasts but one summer'.

CORIANDER
Coriandrum sativum, Umbelliferae

One of the oil-bearing seed plants which used to be grown extensively in England, mostly in the eastern counties, but its production so declined that when supplies were cut off by the Second World War, farmers were asked once again to grow the plant under Government contract.

It grows on a medium or heavy soil, and requires little treatment once the plants are strong enough to make headway. The seed is sown in autumn or spring, although stronger plants are produced by autumn sowing. Harvesting is carried out in August or September, but, like all umbelliferous plants, it has to be cut just when the seed is ripe, or it quickly scatters. The yield of seed sown on a large scale is 10 to 14 cwt. to the acre.

When the production of English seed declined, it was imported from Holland, Russia and Morocco. It is believed that the Romans brought the seed to England from the East, for it has been cultivated and used as a stimulant and spice from very early times. Mention is made of it in the Bible: 'And the manna was as coriander seed'. The name is derived from the Greek '*koris*', a bug, as the scent is supposed to have some similarity to that repulsive insect, but actually, although the scent is strong, it fades to quite a pleasant fragrance when dried.

The plant is an annual, 1–3 feet tall; the lower leaves are fan-shaped and divided, while the upper ones are feathery. The flowers are in small umbels, pale mauve in colour and dainty in appearance. The seed is round, and is used for flavouring liqueurs and confectionery and as an ingredient in mixed spice.

Coriander is quite easy to grow in the herb-garden, and seed can be procured from most nurserymen. It likes a warm, sunny position, ripening about August. Seed should be dried and stored in air-tight tins.

COSTMARY
Chrysanthemum balsamita, Compositae

Culpeper, writing in the sixteenth century, says of Costmary, 'This inhabitant in every garden is well known', but to-day it is one of the least known of all the garden herbs and seldom seen, although the name lingers on like a pleasant scent. Like many other sweet herbs, it came from the East with the triumphant march of the Romans across Europe, and it has been in this country so long that it is quite acclimatised and will grow in a variety of soils. The fact that it does not seed here may account for its disappearance, for propagation has to be effected by root division. This is really an easy matter, as the roots creep underground, like Mint, and soon cover a wide area.

The Tansy, another herb which grows in most soils, is its close relation, but the scent of the leaves and flowers of Costmary has an odour of Balsam, without the sharp pungency of Tansy. Costmary grows about 2 feet tall, with entire leaves and insignificant flowers, which appear only when the plant is grown in full sunlight.

In the days when ale was home-brewed, Costmary was often added to give a sharper tang to the drink, so it received the name of Alecost (*Costis* means a herb with a spicy flavour), and Mary was added in honour of Our Lady, after whom so many plants were named.

Though Culpeper, in singing its praises, tells that 'Taken fasting in the morning, it relieves chronic pains in the head', its old use was mainly for dysentery and ague. It held its place in the *Pharmacopoeia* until the end of the eighteenth century, but is now little used for medicine. It is one of the plants which adds a delicious scent to pot-pourri, intensifying the fragrance of other leaves and blossom.

CUMIN
Cuminum cyminum, Umbelliferae

Even as recently as the last Coronation a pound of cumin seed was offered as a gift to King George VI by Cornishmen. Yet this is now a very unfamiliar plant and is rarely to be seen in herb gardens. This neglect is probably due to tenderness, for it is a native of countries south of the Mediterranean, where the seeds have been valued for many centuries for indigestion, as well as for use in curry and pickles. As the plant is small and inconspicuous, with almost thready stems, growing about one foot tall, it can easily be crowded out by more vigorous herbs.

Gerard says, 'It is a low or base herbe' with 'the spiky tufts at the top of the branches or stalks, of a red or purplish colour, after which come the seed, of a strong or rancke smell, and biting taste'. It is probably its unpleasant taste that has ousted it in favour of the more agreeable Caraway, which has practically the same medicinal properties. In the Middle Ages the stronger and more unpleasant the flavour of a herb the more highly was it esteemed for its curative powers. Tastes have altered considerably since then!

When grown for the herb-garden, it must first be sown in pots, and gradually hardened off in a cold frame, being afterwards transplanted to a warm, sunny bed. Cumin is, however, worth growing, for it is a pretty little plant with umbels of rose-coloured flowers and dark-green, fennel-like leaves.

DILL
Anethum graveolens, Umbelliferae

Everyone has heard of Dill Water, but not everyone knows that the plant which provides this safe and useful remedy for digestive troubles will grow quite easily, even luxuriantly, in English gardens. It is one of the oil-containing seed-herbs which used to be cultivated on the dry soil of eastern England, until importations at much cheaper prices almost forced it out of cultivation.

Coming originally from the sunny Mediterranean lands, it spread across Europe, probably being brought here by the Romans, for mention is made of it in an early Anglo-Saxon Herbal. The name is derived from the Norse word '*dilla*', to lull, for it was believed in early days to be a cure for sleeplessness, while another favourite use for it was to sharpen the appetite. In medicine it is known as '*Fructus Anethi*', and has long been included in the *British Pharmacopoeia*, which directs that the fruits of English-grown Dill are alone to be employed.

Dill is grown as an annual and makes a fairly tall plant, 2 to 3 feet high, with strong, upright stems, feathery leaves rather like those of Fennel, and small umbels of yellow flowers.

As the seed begins to dry, the whole plant turns a purplish-red, and careful watch must then be kept to collect the fruits, as they drop very quickly. The taste of the seed is rather like that of Caraway; in fact, when Caraway was unobtainable for confectionery during the Second World War, Dill was sometimes substituted. But the outer husk of Dill seeds is tougher than that of the soft-fleshed Caraway, and most people were not deceived.

The leaves, chopped finely, may be used in salads, soups, stews and savoury dishes, but a little goes a long way, for the taste is slightly bitter. But made into Dill Vinegar or blended into sauce for fish, the sharpness is not too noticeable. In American cookery leaves and flowers are used with cucumber to give spiciness.

FENNEL
Foeniculum vulgare, Umbelliferae

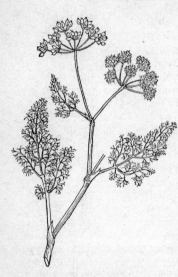

A vigorous-growing tall plant of handsome appearance, often found in cottage gardens, the owners usually remarking that 'it has always been there'. This is a proof that Fennel takes its place with such herbs as Peppermint, Pennyroyal and Sage, which, in the days before synthetic drugs, country people naturally grew to equip their own medicine cupboards.

In Roman times it was held to be a useful vegetable, and Anglo-Saxon Herbals mention it both for its culinary and medicinal uses. Its association with cooked fish is of ancient date, for, as Culpeper says: 'One good old custom is not yet left off, viz., to boil fennel with fish, for it consumes the phlegmatic humours which fish most plentifully afford and annoy the body with'. Another of his remarks is: 'It is much used in drink to make people more lean that are too fat'.

Fennel may be a little difficult to start, but once it gets going it soon becomes a tall, graceful, bushy plant, with light green, strong, shiny stems, and leaves divided up into almost hair-like segments. The flowers are in large umbels of a very bright yellow. The seeds are large and take a little longer to dry than those of Caraway or Dill.

Any soil will suit this herb, although it delights in a really warm spot in the garden. Seed is sown in the spring, and is ready for harvesting by August or September. During the summer the leaves can be cut for culinary use. They have a pleasantly acid taste, giving just the right sharpness to a sauce served with boiled fish. Medicinally it is used for dispersing flatulence, and is one of the constituents of 'gripe water'.

GARLIC
Allium sativum, Amaryllidaceae

Anyone who travels in Italian buses might be forgiven for deciding never to grow this unpleasantly smelling plant, and one can quite appreciate the decision of the old Greeks that people who ate Garlic should not be allowed in the temples of Cybele.

But from early times it has been considered a very useful medicine, and in the Middle Ages in Britain it was believed to be, either by itself, as a 'simple', or mixed with other herbs, one of the cures for leprosy. Lepers were often called 'pilgarlics', as they were made to peel their own garlic, certainly a mark of identity and a means of segregation!

Throughout the ages it was held to have antiseptic properties, and during the 1914–18 War sterilised Sphagnum Moss soaked in Garlic juice was used for suppurating wounds, a reminder of the old method of treating leprous sores. From time to time, even in modern days, Garlic has been claimed to have marvellous properties; now, in addition to its stimulating powers, it is held to be beneficial in digestive complaints and for coughs, colds and asthma.

Cultivation of Garlic is a fairly easy matter, though it needs a finely sifted soil similar to that of an onion-bed. The cloves should be set about 2 in. in the ground about February or March, and lightly covered with soil. The bulbs may usually be lifted during August. There is generally a demand for Garlic from druggists, and good prices have been paid for it.

HYSSOP
Hyssopus officinalis, Labiatae

This plant, although not a native of Britain, will grow luxuriantly in gardens of a light, sandy soil. It is a beautiful herb, with dark evergreen leaves and deep-blue flowers, although there are pink and white varieties. Dioscorides, the ancient Greek physician, calls it '*Azob*' in his *Materia Medica*, referring to it as 'a holy herb', as it was used in the purification ceremonies in the temples. That it was also known to the Jews is proved by the words of the Psalmist: 'Purge me with hyssop and I shall be clean'.

Probably brought here by the Romans for the same purpose, it was later on planted in the monastic gardens for its medical properties. The flower-tops are cut during the blossoming period, about July, and used as an infusion for coughs, colds and bronchial ailments. A colourless oil is also distilled from the leaves, which gives a fine odour to perfumes and liqueurs.

Hyssop is easily cultivated, though it does not thrive well in shade. It can be grown from seed sown in April, or by division of the plants in early spring or autumn, or by cuttings, preferably in spring-time. These young plants merely require watering and weeding until established, and then should go ahead without further trouble, as the plant is quite hardy.

IRIS (FLORENTINE)
Iris florentina, Iridaceae

This glorious plant is not in the strictest sense a herb, but it is so beautiful, with its pale-green, spear-like leaves and lovely, large, white blooms, that it is a great addition to a herb-garden, where so many of the plants are of a somewhat subdued greyish shade. The flowers rise well above the leaves, although the plant is symmetrical in shape.

As the name shows, it originally came from Florence in Italy, where it is said to grow in abundance. It also grows in Mexico, and most of the root is imported from there, but it has settled down quite well to the English climate, and has a long period of blossoming, rather longer than many of the Irises.

It is often called the Fleur de Lis, or Fleur de Louis, being so named after one of the long line of French kings, so France is probably another of its homes. France has also the record of being one of the foremost countries in the perfumery trade, and it is for this purpose that the Florentine Iris is grown.

Its claim to a place in the herb-garden is that its root provides the famous Orris powder, used in all the best toilet cosmetics and perfumes. All so-called 'violet powders' contain Orris root, as the fragrance is very similar to that of sweet violets.

The Florentine Iris can be grown in the open ground in any soil, although it rejoices and gives its best in a sunny spot. The rhizomes are hard, but can be dried quite satisfactorily, if cut in pieces, the rootlets being first cleaned off. When dry, it is grated and pounded and added to a plain starch powder if required as a cosmetic.

LAVENDER
Lavandula vera, Labiatae

Of all the many sweet-scented herbs, Lavender is the one which has endeared itself generally more than any other, often for sentimental reasons rather than practical ones, though, as William Turner said so happily in the sixteenth century, 'it is a comfort to the braine'. So great is its popularity that it is surprising that apparently it was not cultivated in Britain until the middle of the sixteenth century, although it had long grown wild in Provence, and was the favoured 'bath salts' of the Romans, from whom it probably got its name, for *lavandula* comes from the Latin '*lavare*', to wash.

It seems to have been known to Shakespeare, and no doubt he included it with other sweet-smelling herbs in the line 'Smelling as sweet as Bucklersbury in simpling time'; Bucklersbury was the London herb market of Tudor days. Gerard, Culpeper and Parkinson all mention it as 'well known', growing it in their herb gardens; from these it spread to the commercial herb-farms around London, in Surrey, Hertfordshire and Kent, until Lavender production became almost a part of English rural life.

In early times it was used as a digestive and nerve medicine, and this idea is still preserved by the application of Lavender perfume for headaches, toothache, neuralgia and in the sick room, its vigorous, refreshing odour seeming to sweep away grief and melancholy as well as to revive a fainting patient. Lavender is still included in the *British Pharmacopoeia*, and the oil content of the British variety is said to be three times greater than that from foreign plants.

Large quantities of Lavender are still grown in this country, although the poor price paid for a rather variable and difficult crop by the drug firms has greatly reduced the acreage under cultivation, but there is always a steady demand for *L. vera*, both for medicine and perfumery.

There are several species of Lavender in addition to the True Lavender, perhaps the best-known being Spike Lavender, a coarser, broader-leaved variety; the dwarf species, known as Munstead varieties; *Lavendula stoechas*, with a deep purple flower, and *L. alba*, a white variety, not very easy to grow in Britain, and many others. The oils from these different forms of Lavender vary very much in strength and fragrance, and if the plant is to be grown commercially, *Lavandula vera* is considered the best variety.

Lavender needs a sunny position and a light, sandy or gravelly soil for preference, though the fact that it is met with in almost every garden proves it is not fastidious either as to soil or situation. But growth is slower on clay soils, and it does not flower so abundantly. It can be grown from seed, though a much quicker method is from cuttings taken in the autumn and planted out the following spring, or by root division. As Lavender is one of the plants which soon becomes leggy, fresh plantations should regularly be made if a plentiful supply of flowers is needed.

Lavender is mostly used now in perfumery, scents, sachets, soaps and pot-pourri, and it can be added to jams and jellies if proportions are carefully watched.

LAVENDER COTTON
Santolina chamaecyparissus, Compositae

This beautiful plant makes a good addition to a herb-garden as an edging with its striking whitish-grey foliage and flowers like bright yellow balls. It has the further merit of lasting throughout the winter, holding up its sparkling lacy foliage against the drabness of winter decay, and gleaming pale green against the January snows.

Like many other herbs from sunny climes, it grows best in a dry soil and open situation, but it will grow quite well on cold clay, though perhaps not flowering quite so freely. It is one of the smaller herbs which looks at its best if grown in masses.

The name 'Lavender' is quite inaccurate, and its only claim to the title is a faint similarity in the colour of the foliage. Its scent, too, is very different from that of the fragrant 'Lavandula', as it has a rank pungency, so strongly acrid that it is particularly disliked by insects, and even the rapacious clothes moth keeps well away from garments in which sprigs of Lavender Cotton have been laid.

It is much too strong to be used for culinary purposes, but it has been employed for centuries as a vermifuge (worm expellent), especially for children, on account of its gentle effect.

LIQUORICE
Glycyrrhiza glabra, Papilionaceae

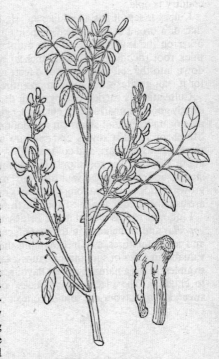

'It is planted in fields and gardens in divers places of this land, and thereof good profit is made', said Culpeper. Gerard, at the end of the sixteenth century, records that Liquorice grew plentifully in his London physic garden, and John Parkinson mentions it as flourishing in his 'pleasant garden' in Holborn, so there is considerable evidence to show that this plant has long been established in Britain. The tradition is that the Black Friars introduced it into Yorkshire when they settled there during the early days of the sixteenth century, and it has remained in cultivation in the district ever since.

It is rather strange that such a useful herb so long established in Britain should not have become more popular, and we can only imagine that the enormous imports which have been sent here from several European countries have almost killed home production.

Cultivation of it is still carried on around Pontefract, its original home, and from this town, too, come those delicious sweetmeats, known as Pontefract cakes, once seen in almost every chemist's shop. But the acreage now under cultivation has decreased by more than half, even though the flavour of the English root is said to be far superior to that of the Continental product.

The quaint name of Liquorice is a corruption of its generic name, given it by the Greek doctor Dioscorides ('*glukos*', sweet, and '*rhiza*', root), and it is still commonly called 'Liquorish' by country people.

Culpeper says it has a leaf like an ash, but it is also similar to that of a broad bean, the leaflets being arranged opposite each other on the leaf-stalk, with pale purple flowers and a strong, thick root (dividing up into branches), which sometimes goes down into the soil to a depth of 4 feet; not an easy root to lift, for it is of greater value if taken up entire.

Cultivation is carried out by using the old crowns not sufficiently good for pharmacists, cut to a length of 4 inches, and runners or underground stems cut to about 4 inches. Planting is in March or April. Crowns and sets are arranged in groups of three, 12 inches apart, and covered lightly with soil to a depth of about 3 inches. The soil should be dry and loamy and free from stones, and needs to be well dug and manured and the plants grown in ridges, so that long rootstocks can develop. The plants are usually lifted in the third and fourth years during autumn.

Liquorice root is official in the British and American *Pharmacopoeias* and is included in the manufacture of pastilles, tablets and cough mixtures, as it has soothing and demulcent properties valuable in cases of sore throat, quinsy, laryngitis and bronchial troubles. It has a naturally sweet flavour, and can safely be given to children. The black, shiny 'sticks' of liquorice with their sweet, strong flavour are sold in confectioners' shops.

LOVAGE
Levisticum officinale, Umbelliferae

This is one of the sweet herbs which was once grown a great deal more than it is to-day, the term '*officinale*' showing that it dates at least from monastic times and that the monks found it useful medicinally. Like Parsley and other herb-plants, it comes from southern Europe, growing plentifully in the mountains near the French sea-coast.

It is a hardy perennial plant, and will grow to a height of 3 to 4 feet in fairly rich soil. The stems are thick and hollow, and with the same translucent green as the Angelica. In fact, in many ways it resembles Angelica, but the flavour and scent, though sweetly pungent, are not quite so aromatic. Its taste is often said to be a cross between celery and parsley.

The flowers appear in June, and are large umbels of tiny yellow florets, followed by small, spicy, brownish seeds. A resinous yellow juice is extracted from the stems.

Seed is sown in autumn or spring, or the plant may be propagated by root division. Seedlings or young plants need a clean seed-bed of rich, moist soil; they will then go ahead quite happily and last for several years.

Once Lovage was valued as a medicine for sore throats and quinsy, and for bathing inflamed eyes, Culpeper saying, 'It removes spots or freckles'. But its main use now is in confectionery, the young stems being preserved in the same way as those of Angelica, but they are rather more stringy and less exciting in flavour than that plant.

MARIGOLD
Calendula officinalis, Compositae

Culpeper aptly calls the Marigold 'a herb of the Sun', and the name '*calendula*' was given it in the belief that it may be seen on the Calends (or first day) of every month in the year; '*officinalis*' shows it to be one of the old monkish herbs. Long ago this delightful plant came to Britain from some sunny clime, but has settled down here like a native, becoming useful both as a culinary and medicinal herb.

Shakespeare refers to it as the 'marigold that goes to bed with the sun and with him rises weeping', pointing out its habit of opening early in the morning in fine weather and when wet closing its petals until the sun shines again. In India, probably its earliest home, its golden glory and sun-loving ways have made it a sacred flower, and gods and goddesses are adorned with wreaths of Marigolds.

Though large, showy varieties of these plants have been developed by gardeners, it is the old-fashioned orange blossoms that are wanted for pharmacy. The sixteenth-century herbalists used it 'in possets, broths and drinks as a comforter to the heart', and modern medicine finds it useful as a stimulant, for inducing perspiration in fevers, and for bronchial ailments.

Both flowers and leaves are collected and dried, and though Marigold petals need careful handling, almost resembling cut tobacco when properly finished, large amounts of them were gathered during the Second World War, and in some cases sent direct to hospitals. The fresh petals may be sprinkled on salads, giving a piquant flavour and a delightful appearance.

MARJORAM
Origanum onites, Labiatae

Origanum comes from two Greek words, '*oros*', mountain, and '*ganos*', joy, referring to this plant's native home along sunny south European shores, where it spreads itself with bright rose-purple flowers and wind-blown fragrance. But it came to

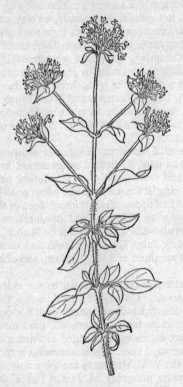

Britain so long ago that it is now recognised as one of the usual culinary herbs.

There are several varieties, the oldest and best known being the Pot or Perennial Marjoram (*Origanum onites*), known to Pliny, the early monkish doctors, and those famous herbalists of the sixteenth and seventeenth centuries, Gerard, Culpeper and Parkinson, who grew it in their London 'Physick Gardens', and used it both for culinary and medicinal purposes.

Though all varieties have much in common, this species is distinguished by its more spreading form, by a warm reddish tinge on stems and leaves, and by the fact that the whorls of lilac flowers appear rather late, at the end of July and August.

All the Marjorams love a sunny position and a dry soil, though they will grow, not quite so luxuriantly, on clay and in shadier places. Pot Marjoram may be grown from seed sown in March and April, from cuttings or by root divisions of well-grown plants during the spring. The plants are perennial, about 2 feet high, and will continue growing for years in a garden if properly cared for. Commercially, the whole herb is cut down as soon as flowering starts, hung in bunches and dried. When this is done, seed must be sown annually to get a good supply of strong plants, even though the plants spring up again from the roots the following year.

Sweet or Knotted Marjoram (*Origanum majorana*) is a more tender plant, and must be treated as an annual in Britain, for cold weather and frost usually kill it. Gerard calls it 'sweet marjerome', saying 'it has a marvellous sweet smell', but that 'it perisheth at the first approach of Winter'. Seed of this variety is sown indoors during February and outdoors in April. The flowers are greyish-white in tight heads or 'knots', blossoming in June and early July. The leaves, oval and dark green, are slightly larger than those of Pot Marjoram, and of a sweet pungent scent.

Another variety, sometimes grown as an indoor plant, is *Origanum dictamnus*, 'Dittany of Crete', a delicate plant with slender stems, downy leaves and small, pink flowers.

All the Marjorams have aromatic oil, used mostly for perfumery. They are extensively cultivated in France, but have become rather neglected here. This is somewhat surprising, as the Perennial and the Wild Marjoram are quite easy to grow, and give just that extra pungency to 'Mixed Herbs', that full-flavoured bouquet of Mint, Sage, Parsley, Thyme and Marjoram. Marjoram is little used now in medicine, except as a 'Spring Tea', though it has tonic and stimulating properties.

MINT

Mentha viridis, Labiatae

The Mints almost need a book to themselves, and those who wish to make a study of this plant should read the publications of the late Mr. F. Fraser, a leading authority on Mints. To many of us, Mint is just a pleasant, accommodating herb which comes up every year and supplies us with that delicate savoury, Mint Sauce.

As a matter of fact there are many kinds of Mint, and in normal times they are grown to quite a large extent by horticulturists and market-gardeners, for Mint is one of the plants which can be forced in greenhouses for the early market in January to March.

As the result of a survey, it was found that a number of varieties of Mint were being grown commercially in many English counties. The Ministry of Agriculture can give information regarding large-scale cultivation of these Mints, with details of a disease, Mint Rust, which may attack the plants and cause wholesale destruction.

Mint has been known as a useful herb since very early days, and the reference in the New Testament to tithes of Mint, Cumin and Anise shows that even then the plant was a valuable commodity.

The Romans made great use of Mint, probably bringing it to these islands. During the Middle Ages it was a favourite strewing herb, and the sharp, sweet scent must have been like a refreshing breeze in the stuffy atmosphere of the houses. Mint became one of the most popular herbs through the centuries, so that now almost everyone with a garden has a patch of Mint.

Though it prefers a damp situation, it will grow almost anywhere, but a sheltered, warm spot will help the plants to start growth earlier in the year. Cultivation is by root division in the spring, cuttings during the summer and by layering the roots.

Stalks should be cut for drying just as the flowers appear, several being bunched together and dried either in a warm outhouse or in the kitchen. The leaves dry quickly and can soon be rubbed down; they should be put through a sieve and powdered if sold in packed form.

The best-known species is Spearmint, with sharp-pointed, deep green leaves, though the Round-Leaved Mint (*Mentha rotundifolia*) or Apple Mint, with a hairy, roundish leaf, has a more delicate flavour. There are other varieties and hybrids, each with its own particular scent, which are well worth growing.

Mint is mostly grown as a culinary herb, for Mint sauce has never lost its popularity, and a sprig of Mint is the proper accompaniment in the cooking of new potatoes and green peas. Mint jelly, Mint drinks, Mint salads are excellent additions to meals, and Mint tea is a safe home cure for indigestion. As a medicine, Mint is official in the British and other *Pharmacopoeias* for the alleviation of digestive troubles and as a stimulant.

PARSLEY
Petroselinum crispum, Umbelliferae

Culpeper has a delightful habit of saying 'This herbe is so well known it needs no description'. Certainly this might apply to Parsley, for it is the best-known and the most cultivated of all the sweet herbs, and has long been used as a garnish in meat and

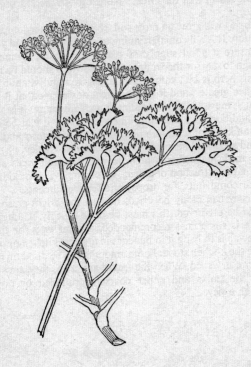

fish shops, around sandwiches and, of course, in the inevitable Parsley Sauce.

As it often grew on rocky soil, the old Greeks named it '*petroselinum*', '*petros*' meaning a rock. They believed it to have sprung from the blood of a hero, Archemorus, the forerunner of death, so Parsley was held sacred to the dead, and wreaths of it were laid on tombs.

There is no actual wild form of this plant in Britain though various other members of the umbelliferous family go by this name. Gardeners now grow the variety known as Curled Parsley, so that there is no fear of confusion with Fool's Parsley, a poisonous little weed somewhat resembling it, which sometimes appears in the vegetable or flower garden. Fool's Parsley, however, has white flowers, and a very unpleasant scent, and so bitter are the leaves that the Greeks named it 'Aethusa', from 'aitho', 'I burn.'

Parsley will grow on most soils, but it prefers a damp, shaded position. It is a biennial, running to seed in the second year, and to ensure a good supply of plants during the summer with enough to dry for the winter, yearly sowings should be made.

This herb is best eaten fresh, as its iron and vitamin content are then greater, and it has the great advantage that it will live through most winters. Its culinary uses are many; it is an excellent addition to salads and, finely chopped, it can be blended with all kinds of sandwich fillings. Soups and stews and savouries and sauces all benefit by a little chopped Parsley.

Its medicinal value is high, leaves, root and seeds all being used in the extraction of a drug, apiol, employed for kidney and similar complaints, for dropsy and female ailments.

Parsley can easily be dried, but, as the bright-green colour should be preserved, this must be done quickly. Though oven-drying is sometimes recommended, a surer way for the busy housewife is to hang it in bunches in a warm kitchen or on trays above the kitchen stove. Large amounts can be dried on racks in a warm, dry shed. When the leaves are crisp, they are stripped from the stalks and either coarsely crumbled or powdered through a sieve.

PEPPERMINT
Mentha piperita, Labiatae

The various species of Mint are not always easy to distinguish, and this plant may be confused with a coarse variety (*Mentha longifolia*), Horse Mint, which also grows wild in damp places. Peppermint, both the black and the white variety, is a delicate, slender plant, about a foot tall, with lance-shaped, sharply cut leaves and small heads of purple flowers.

The black variety has deep purple stems and dark olive-green foliage, the white variety has green stems and light-green leaves and is usually of less vigorous growth. Both kinds are of value medicinally, though the oil derived from the white peppermint is of a finer quality and fetches a better price than that from black mint.

On the other hand, the black variety is the more robust, and is the sort usually cultivated in Britain. Though large amounts are imported, considerable quantities have always been grown here, Mitcham in Surrey, Market Deeping in Lincolnshire and Hitchin in Hertfordshire having been important centres.

When grown in the herb garden, Peppermint should be given the dampest and richest part, though too much shade is not desirable, or the plants will grow weedy with a sparseness of leaves, and as it is the leaves that are needed for medicine, shrubby plants are required.

Everyone knows the value of Peppermint, both for flavouring unpleasantly tasting medicine, and for tablets, sweets and pastilles for digestive complaints. Peppermint tea is a home-made medicine which has never lost favour. The whole of the herb contains valuable oils, chief among them being menthol. The plant is cut about the second week in August, dried and stripped of its leaves. For home use, the dried product is stored in tins or tightly stoppered glass jars.

POPPY
Papaver somniferum, Papaveraceae

Originally the Opium Poppy came from the East – Persia, India and China – but it has been cultivated for centuries in Europe, and spread to Britain many years ago.

This lovely plant has greyish-green leaves, and tall, stout stalks from which swing the green buds, later to be succeeded by a quickly passing flower. The plump heads are greenish-white, soon ripening to light brown. Poppies prefer a rich, moist, well-cultivated soil, which is one reason why they thrive so well in our herbaceous borders. A clump or row of them in the herb-garden will provide a pleasant patch of colour during the summer, but ruthless measures must be taken in cutting the seed-heads.

Opium is extracted from the unripe heads, cuts being made in the outer skin, and the white, milky juice scraped out. This is formed into cakes and dried in the sun, when it becomes deep brown. Though the Poppy has been cultivated in Britain since 1798, it has never been grown for the extraction of opium, as only plants grown in hot, sunny climates produce this drug.

Morphine, one of the world's most valuable medicines, is a product of opium, getting this name from Morpheus, the God of Sleep. But the Poppy is also grown very largely for its heads, as they are employed in the making of sedative drugs for external inflammation and included in cough medicines. As the seeds do not contain morphine, they are used in European countries in confectionery, being sprinkled on cakes, rolls and bread, giving a faint spicy flavour.

Poppy-heads have long been a rural remedy for toothache, neuralgia and other nervous pains, and once it was common to see bunches of the dried heads hanging in chemists' shops. The Poppy, as the source of many valuable alkaloids, is official in the *British Pharmacopoeia*.

RHUBARB
Rheum officinale, Polygonaceae

The variety of Rhubarb used in pharmacy is the Turkey or Chinese Rhubarb (*Rheum palmatum*), a strong, tall plant of 8 feet or more, with coarsely toothed leaves, divided like a duck's foot, and whitish flowers in a loose spray. The root grows quickly, becoming very large.

Though attempts have been made to cultivate this variety in England, there has been little success owing to the tendency of the roots to rot. But since the middle of the eighteenth century *Rheum officinale* has been grown in the Banbury district, in Bedfordshire and West Suffolk, analysis having shown that the same medicinal properties are common to both kinds. The Garden Rhubarb (*Rheum rhaponticum*), grown for its red leaf-stalks for preserves and pickles, contains these properties to a very limited extent. The medicinal variety is a tall, slender plant with green buds and leaf-stalks and small white flowers.

The root, the source of the drug, is lifted during the autumn, cut into smallish pieces and hung on strings to dry in the sun, afterwards being finished off in heat. The drug produced from Rhubarb is valuable, and the plant has long been included in the *British Pharmacopoeia*. It is tonic and astringent, is one of the ingredients of 'Gregory powder', and has been found very effective in cases of dysentery.

When the plant was first used as a fruit about a hundred years ago it appears that both the leaves and flowers were cooked as a vegetable, but research during recent times has shown that the leaves contain a dangerous substance, oxalic acid, and should on no account be used for food.

The red leaf-stalks also contain oxalic acid in very small quantities, and are not considered suitable for people subject to rheumatism and gout.

ROSEMARY
Rosmarinus officinalis, Labiatae

Shakespeare's much-quoted line 'There's rosemary, that's for remembrance' had its origin in the old custom of carrying wreaths of rosemary at funerals. Thomas Hood speaks of it as 'Rosemary that always mourns the dead'. And possibly Shakespeare had heard, too, of the Greek students who twined Rosemary in their hair when studying for examinations! Even as late as the nineteenth century a few Rosemary sprigs were always carried in a bridal bouquet.

Shakespeare's reference to Rosemary was well understood by his audience, for in Elizabethan times gardens great and small grew this herb, not only for its sentimental associations, but also because it was held in high esteem for beautifying the hair and for preventing baldness, just as to-day Rosemary is included in all the best hair-oils and hair-washes. It is said that the oil in the leaves has a stimulating effect on the hair-glands, and for the same reason is beneficial in nervous headaches.

Rosemary, the 'dew of the sea', was loved by the Greeks and Romans, and no doubt the latter people brought it to Britain, for it has never grown there in a wild state, but has been cultivated for its 'vertues' throughout the ages.

Propagation is either by root divisions, cuttings or seeds. Cuttings taken in August and planted in a dry, sandy soil in a sunny position should be ready by the following autumn for planting in their permanent home. But it is a very slow-growing plant, and the great grey bushes sprinkled twice a year with powder-blue blossoms seen in old gardens must have been there many a long day. It will grow in almost any soil, but the plants have a greater wealth of flowers and a more fragrant scent if set in a sunny plot on a light, sandy soil.

Oil of Rosemary is much used in perfumery, and the delicious odour of genuine eau-de-Cologne is largely due to this sweet-scented herb. Soaps, powders and pot-pourris also owe some of their charm to this gracious plant.

Rosemary is included in the *British Pharmacopoeia*, for use in tonic medicines, as a nervine and for digestive disorders. Provided proportions are watched, finely chopped leaves and flowers may be added to soup, and they give a rare taste to salads.

It is easy to dry, and will retain its scent for several years if packed in tins or airtight jars.

RUE

Ruta graveolens, Rutaceae

The almost complete stoppage of imports of vital drugs during the Second World War has led to considerable research with various herbs, not only in Britain, but also in America. Over a century ago, rutin, the essential principle of Rue, was isolated,

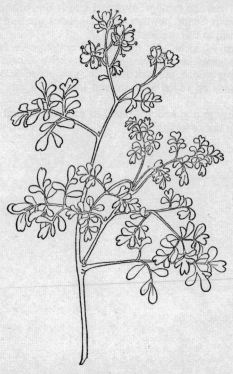

but its full medicinal value was not realised until recently, when experiments by the United States Department of Agriculture showed that this was a drug of considerable effect in the treatment of weakened blood-vessels causing high blood pressure. It is also believed that rutin will be an aid to nutrition by contributing to the hardness of teeth and bones.

As the cultivation of Rue on a large scale might be slow and uncertain, Buckwheat, a well-known, quickly-growing American crop, which also contains rutin, is being grown to a great extent for its production, as it was estimated that 10,000 lb. of rutin would be required for medical purposes in 1946.

Though in the past the exact medicinal content of Rue was not known, it has been held for centuries to be a useful drug; in fact, the name given it by the Greeks, '*Ruta*', means 'to set free'. Its old name, 'Herb of Grace', also emphasises its medical purpose.

Shakespeare refers to it in *Richard III* – 'Here in this place I'll set a bank of Rue, sour herb of grace', and Culpeper says, 'It is well known', and proceeds to catalogue almost every ailment and pain of the body, ascribing Rue as a certain cure. It was believed that an infusion of Rue benefited the eyes, Milton mentions 'Euphrasy and Rue' as given by the Angel to restore Adam's sight. It is now prescribed for nervous diseases and women's ailments.

Rue is often found in cottage gardens, and, as it is much too bitter for culinary purposes, this is proof that it has long been cultivated as a medicine, and also for its power in keeping away unpleasant insects, including fleas. The Law Courts were formerly strewn with Rue, and the plant was twined round the judge's chair, not only to discourage vermin, but also to act as a disinfectant in the germ-laden air surrounding the prisoners taken from the insanitary jails.

Rue is a striking plant, with much-divided, greyish-green leaves and gay yellow flowers. The scent, though strong, is not unpleasant. There are several varieties, a very lovely one being variegated.

Though its original home was southern Europe, it is quite hardy in Britain, and probably by now well acclimatised, for it will stand any amount of frost, and rises quite undaunted after being buried in the snow. Cultivation can be by seed in the spring, cuttings or root division. The last-named way is possibly the best, as it has the advantage of dividing up old plants, thus giving renewed strength.

SAGE
Salvia officinalis, Labiatae

'Eat Sage in May and you'll live for aye' may seem a nice-sounding jingle, but there is a good deal of truth behind it. Many old people in country districts ascribe their long life and

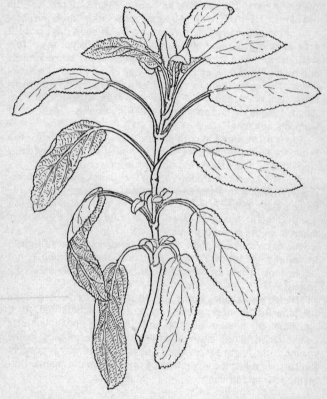

good health to Sage tea in spring and autumn, to Sage sandwiches for breakfast and supper, or chopped Sage added to porridge.

The name Sage comes from the Latin word '*salveo*', I am well, for the Romans, borrowing the habit from the Greeks, introduced Sage into many of their dishes and may have been the originators of Sage stuffing with rich meats, such as pork and duck. Along the shores of the Mediterranean, Sage grows luxuriantly over the hillsides, and the collection of the plant is a rural industry.

The Romans brought their healthful Sage to all the lands they conquered, including Britain, where it adapted itself quite happily to our cold, wind-swept country. From the gardens of the conquerors it passed on to the monkish 'herbaries' and so to perhaps almost every garden in the land, for where is there a garden in which Sage is not found?

Two well-known varieties are cultivated – the narrow-leaved and the broad-leaved – as well as the lesser-known Red Sage, its shoots beautifully tinged with purple, and usually employed in medicine. Cultivation of Sage is very simple, as it will grow anywhere, even under trees, though it makes more luxuriant growth in a warm, sunny spot. In fact, it is such an accommodating plant that it is apt to be neglected in some gardens, being allowed to grow into untidy, straggling bushes with a great deal of woody stem, taking up valuable space and producing little good leaf.

Cuttings or root divisions of Sage plants may be made about every three to five years, and these should be brought on in a sheltered situation and kept well weeded and watered. As the plants are to live in the same place for several years, they should be planted at least 12 inches apart each way. A good Sage bed is always valuable, not only for culinary and medicinal uses in the home, but dried Sage, either in bunches or rubbed down and packed in cellulose bags, has always a ready sale in shops.

All the Sages have a medicinal value. Culpeper says, 'It is of excellent use to help the memory, warming and quickening the senses'. But he is also very enthusiastic about its power to cure all the many diseases from which even seventeenth-century man could suffer.

Nowadays it is mostly used as a gargle and mouthwash, for keeping the teeth white, as a stimulant and for digestive ailments. Sage tea, a favourite country drink, is made by pouring a pint of boiling water on an ounce of Sage leaves, and allowing it to stand two hours or so before being drunk. It is a fine tonic, and probably has a soothing effect in nervous ailments. Sage vinegar for a gargle is similarly made, except that $\frac{1}{2}$ pint of hot malt vinegar is substituted for the boiling water and another $\frac{1}{2}$ pint of cold water is added. Shake well and allow to stand until required.

SALAD BURNET
Poterium sanguisorba, Rosaceae

Even though this dainty little plant is found wild, it deserves a place in the herb-garden, for it is quite useful in the kitchen. Unfortunately it is usually so happy in the good garden soil that it spreads rather vigorously, and may rather overlap its own area. Still, it can be kept within bounds by cutting back shoots and by preventing it from seeding.

It grows about a foot high, standing well upright, with separate leaflets on long stalks, small, reddish flowers and stems and an almost berry-like fruit. Propagation may be by seed, by root division in spring or autumn, or, much more simply, by digging up some of the wild plants which grow in profusion in many parts but chiefly on chalk downs. It will soon settle down in the herb-garden, though it likes light and air.

The name '*poterium*' comes from the Greek '*poterion*', a drinking-cup or tankard, pointing to its early use as an addition to wine and other drinks, to which it gave a delightful cucumber flavour. Culpeper prescribes that 'Two or three of the stalks with leaves put into a cup of wine, especially claret, are known to quicken the spirits, refresh and clear the heart and drive away melancholy'. It was also considered to be a 'woundeherbe, either inward or outward'.

Salad Burnet always had a place in Tudor herb-gardens, and was often planted along the narrow little pathways with Thyme and Mint, so that, when trodden on, the fragrance was an additional pleasure. Its present use is mainly for salads and sauces. In medicine it is used as a tonic. This herb is listed as one of those taken by the Pilgrim Fathers on their long trail to the New World.

SAVORY (SUMMER)
Satureia hortensia, Labiatae

Both the Savories were introduced from southern Europe to Britain during the sixteenth century, and at once became favourite flavouring herbs, being of pleasant delicate taste.

The great advantage of having two Savories is that while the Summer one grows up quickly, flowers early and is soon ready to dry, the Winter Savory carries on during the wet and dreary months of the year with quite a good selection of leaves.

Summer Savory is an annual with a seed of that useful kind which will germinate even after having been forgotten a year, or longer. It is sown in April in a light, not rich, soil and sunny position. The seeds are rather slow in germinating, and then grow into plants barely a foot high. Flowers are small and heliotrope, and as soon as they appear the plant should be cut and dried; drying is a fairly simple matter.

Savory has a distinctive but very pleasant flavour, and can be used in all kinds of stuffings, in sausages, meat dishes and, of course, cooked with broad beans, peas, fresh and dried varieties. Occasionally it is infused as a digestive medicine, but the drug trade makes little use of it.

SAVORY (WINTER)
Satureia montana, Labiatae

This plant will, if properly cultivated, grow almost into a small shrub, and is quite an addition to a herb-garden or the herbaceous border, for though the flowers are small and dimly lilac, the whole plant is quite decorative with its spear-pointed, deep green leaves, dark, woody stems and compact habit of growth.

It does best in a poor, stony soil; in fact, it quickly deteriorates if given a rich manured part of the garden. As its specific name '*montana*' shows, its native home is on hills, where the soil is apt to be rather rough.

Cuttings can be taken of strong shoots with a heel, or the roots may be divided in the spring, especially if the plants are getting over-large and straggly; or it may be grown from seed. Seedlings and cuttings are best planted out in wet weather. Since Savory is so easy to grow it is surprising that one so seldom finds it in our kitchen gardens.

Culpeper puts the two Savories together in his description, saying they are 'good for colic', but Winter Savory is no longer used in medicine. In France and Belgium Winter Savory is often blended with meat dishes and is considered especially good with trout. The word 'savoury' aptly describes this plant, and it can be used either dry or fresh, with due care to its rather uncommon flavour, in cheese and egg dishes or such delicacies as stuffed Marrow, while it is excellent with Tomato Sauce.

SOUTHERNWOOD
Artemisia abrotanum, Compositae

No garden is complete without a clump or two of Southernwood with its feathery, grey-green leaves and sweetly penetrating scent. It was brought to England in that time of great herbal excitement, the Elizabethan period, and soon spread all over the country. And now every country nosegay is adorned with a few sprigs of Lad's Love. It may have been this custom of adding Southernwood to bouquets shyly offered by man to maid as a token of affection, that gave it this delightful name. Its whiskery greyness suggests at once its title of 'Old Man'.

Southernwood is a corruption of southern wormwood, as its home is in southern lands, while the bitter, hardy wormwoods come from the bleak northerly parts of the world.

Propagation is made usually by cuttings, branches 9 to 12 inches long being broken off in April, the leaves stripped to half the length of the cutting, and the stalk then buried in light, gravelly soil. Southernwood does not produce seed in Britain.

The taste of the leaves is bitter, and they contain an essential oil, absinthol, used in tonics, antiseptics and for expelling worms. It is this same rank oil which has a deterrent effect on such objectionable insects as clothes moths and fleas.

SWEET CICELY
Myrrhis odorata, Umbelliferae

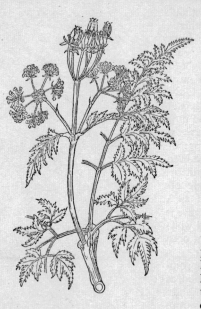

This is a tall, beautiful plant, often growing to a height of 5 feet in a favourable situation, and so ornamental that it is sometimes included in the herbaceous border. Other names for it are the Fern-leaved Chervil, or the Giant Sweet Chervil, but it is a much taller, stouter plant than the real Chervil, and has fern-like leaves and white flowers in large umbels. Sometimes it is found growing wild in the mountainous pastures in the north of England or Wales, and has been known for centuries among north-country people as a useful herb plant. The sweet-scented leaves are supposed to smell like Myrrh, a plant from which a gum-resin, faintly like camphor, is obtained.

It does well in a sunny position, but is not particular as to soil, though it prefers a rough stony or chalky ground. The stems are stout, thick and hollow, and the plant at first sight looks rather like Field Parsley.

Culpeper says: 'It groweth like the Hemlock, but of a fresher green colour, tasting as sweet as the aniseed'. He also mentions its 'pleasantness in salads'. During the sixteenth and seventeenth centuries the roots were boiled like parsnips, and according to Gerard 'dressed how the cunning Cooke knoweth better than myselfe'. Culpeper finishes a catalogue of its virtues with the remark, 'It is so harmless you cannot use it amiss'.

Both root and herb are recommended for coughs and flatulence, and mild digestive ailments.

TARRAGON
Artemisia dracunculus, Compositae

Tarragon is a plant for the herb-garden more for its beautiful form and colour than for its practical 'vertues', which are small compared with some of the sweeter-tasting herbs. For, as Gerard wisely said, 'Tarragonis not to be eaten alone in sallades, but joyned with other herbs, as Lettuce, that it may also temper the coldness of them'.

The pleasant but quaint name of Tarragon is a corruption of the French '*esdragon*', meaning a 'little dragon'. It is difficult to see any connection between this graceful plant and the fearsome dragon, until one remembers that in very early times, snakes and reptiles and noxious insects were much more prevalent than they are to-day. Tarragon was one of the 'Dragon Herbs' which could cure wounds from these creatures as well as 'madde dogges'.

There are two varieties: the French Tarragon, a smallish plant with deep-green leaves and a spicy flavour, often called the True Tarragon, and the Russian Tarragon, with brighter, rougher leaves and a ranker taste. Tarragon likes a sunny position, but is content with poor soil; damp or rich ground may cause it to die out during the winter. As it seldom seeds in Britain, it is propagated by root divisions or cuttings taken in spring or summer.

The leaves may be plucked when needed for cooking, and the whole herb cut and dried in early autumn, though the sharp flavour is rather lost in the dried plant. Tarragon vinegar can be made by steeping the leaves in white vinegar.

This herb is grown commercially in some English counties, for oil of tarragon, for vinegar and for inclusion in what is known as French or Continental mustard. It is also the correct flavouring for the pungent but delicious 'Sauce Tartare'.

THISTLE (HOLY or BLESSED)

Cardenia benedicta, Compositae

This herb is not really a Thistle, its only connection with those spiny plants being that it belongs to the same large family. It is not native to Britain, but has been cultivated there since very early times, as it is mentioned by the Venerable Bede, whose connection with it is believed to have given it the claim to sanctity. A recipe of the thirteenth century for recovery from a dangerous wound prescribes an infusion of Holy Thistle to be drunk for nine mornings with a liberal diet of wheaten bread and milk – the diet probably being as effective as the drug!

In medieval times it was believed to be a cure-all, being recommended even for the plague. Shakespeare says, 'Get you some of this distilled Carduus benedictus and lay it to your heart', and the Elizabethan herbalists asserted that it was 'a preservative against all disease'. Since those days its 'vertues' have considerably diminished, but herbalists now employ it as a tonic, for inducing perspiration and for female complaints.

Apart from any medicinal value, it is a beautiful addition to a herb-garden, or the herbaceous border, for it grows about 3 feet tall, has slim reddish stems, large, dark-green serrated leaves and yellow flowers growing close among the foliage. Propagation is by seed, as it is an annual, and it will do well in almost any soil. It is often sold by nurserymen under the name of '*Carduus benedictus*'.

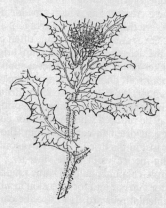

THYME

Thymus vulgaris, Labiatae

Thyme is one of the few plants known by its botanical name, supposed to be derived from a Greek word meaning 'to fumigate', as one of the old uses of the herb was as a form of incense to drive away undesirable insects, with which our ancestors seem to have been plagued.

Its strong, sweet scent and abundance of nectar have an irresistible attraction for bees, and some of this herb should always be planted near the hives, for Thyme honey has had a reputation for centuries as being one of the finest kinds. There are many varieties of Thyme, and each has its own distinct alluring fragrance and flavour. Some of the small varieties can be grown between crazy pavements, or on paths, and, when trodden, fill the air with their delightful odour.

For many centuries Thyme has been included in the front rank of culinary herbs, though perhaps it was valued more in the days before vinegar sauces were used for every kind of meat and fish to make them tasty. But once it has been experimented with in stuffings and savoury dishes it will no longer be overlooked. Roast meat and poultry were once rubbed with Thyme before being put in the oven, giving a quite inimitable taste to the food.

Garden Thyme, a development of the Wild Thyme, is the variety usually grown in gardens, a perennial with a tough, woody root and hard stems rising 12 to 18 inches, with tiny, dark green leaves and whorls of heliotrope flowers. Two varieties are grown commercially, the narrow-leaved and the broad-leaved, as well as a variegated sort. Caraway Thyme is a low-growing variety, which quickly spreads, and has a distinct odour of Caraway. Lemon Thyme is a smaller plant than Garden Thyme, with a delicious odour of lemon. Its leaves are larger than those of Garden Thyme, and it has a creeping habit of growth. Another variety is Silver Thyme, a dainty little plant for edgings, with a whitish-green leaf and a rather faint odour.

The method of cultivation is the same for all varieties, as they are all hardy and will survive the winter, but they prefer a warm situation, and light, stony soil, and they love chalky ground. A good deal of flavour is lost if the plants are grown on cold clay, and they may die out.

Propagation is by divisions of the old plants or by cuttings taken during spring or early summer. As old plants are apt to become woody if left too long, frequent root division is beneficial. Another method is by layering side-shoots early in the year and planting out in the autumn.

In addition to its importance as a culinary herb, varieties of Thyme supply a valuable oil, thymol, used in various kinds of medicine. This plant has in greater or less amount antiseptic properties and forms an ingredient of some mild disinfectants, as well as entering into the composition of bronchial and digestive medicines.

Thyme is one of the easiest plants to dry, and if carefully dried and stored will preserve its piquant aromatic scent for some years.

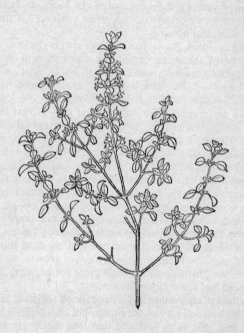

THE HERB-GARDEN

JOHN PARKINSON, three hundred years ago, spoke of his herb-garden in Holborn as 'A Garden of Pleasure'. Our herb-gardens to-day will certainly be pleasant places, but they may even be something more: 'A Garden of Remembrance' of some loved one, dimly fragrant with scented leaves and blossoming flowers, shimmering white Chervil, pale lilac Marjoram and Mint, mist-blue Rosemary, pearly Iris, bright purple Lavender, and, over all and everlastingly, the greys and blues and greens of foliage which never dies.

Or they may be 'Gardens of Memory' – of slips and rootlets collected from friends, Chamomile gathered on Cornish cliffs, Fennel from a sea-washed garden, Marjoram brought from sunny chalk hillsides, Peppermint from a lush plot beside a stream, Costmary and Lovage from the pleasaunce of an ancient manor-house, and other herbs with their lovely names, each with its hallowed memory of place and person.

Beekeepers, too, make their herb-gardens within easy reach of the hives, so that, even on dull windy days, the patient bees may be able to reach great stores of nectar and pollen from Thyme, Marjoram, Lavender, Bergamot (sometimes called Bee Balm), White Horehound, Rosemary and Chervil, together with the Lime-trees which hang their enticing honey-sweet tassels along the hedge. And if in that hedge there are also Bird Cherry and Wild Cherry, Myrobalan Plums, Crab Apple and Rowan trees, the bees have a valuable addition to their sources of supply and will bring to the hives a honey golden-yellow and full of sweet flavours.

Or the herb-garden may be strictly a practical affair, with plants set in orderly rows, so that cuttings and divisions can be easily taken, seed-bearing plants arranged to the best advantage, flowering plants, Marigold and Borage, ready to hand for the gathering, and the duller plants, valued for their roots in a separate plot, so that disturbance in autumn may not be too noticeable.

Apart from the picturesque side of a herb-garden, there is much to be said for it from the strictly utilitarian point of view.

Food can be very dull and monotonous unless properly flavoured, and though it is now the habit to stimulate that savour by deluging meat and vegetable dishes with strongly-spiced sauce, anyone who has tried the alternative method of flavouring with sweet herbs will wholeheartedly vote this the better way.

A great merit of the herb-garden is that it can take so many forms; it can vary in size from window-boxes, through herb paths, herb borders and herb corners, to the spacious and well-planned 'Paradise', as the old sixteenth-century people named their physick gardens. And a very good suggestion has been put forward by the Ministry of Agriculture for allotments to be 'finished' by rows of the best known and most needed herbs. But, whatever form your garden takes, the same points as regards soil, position, cultivation and arrangement have to be considered.

ASPECT OF GARDEN

From the careful plotting of the old monastic and Elizabethan days the growing of herbs in gardens has gradually degenerated, largely owing to the erroneous idea that herbs would grow anywhere. So the few plants that were grown were often put away in any odd corner, and their survival was often due to sheer luck or to the amazing tenacity of the herbs in struggling along somehow. But the results were always poor; Mint, after a few years, would either develop 'rust' and die out altogether or become a few long, leggy stems with attentuated, flavourless leaves, while Sage, as well as Rosemary and Lavender, if left to themselves, made straggly growth, which spoilt their appearance and devitalised the plants.

As the majority of the sweet herbs, Sage, Thyme, Parsley, Mint and Rosemary, came originally from the stony but sunny shores of the Mediterranean, they do not need a rich soil; in fact, they prefer fairly poor ground, but if not attended to and renewed from time to time, they are apt to lose their luxurious growth and their sharp spicy taste and volatile oils quickly deteriorate. Medicinal plants, too, will have a distinct loss of their chemical elements if not grown under the right conditions.

The aspect of the garden or border is of first importance, and though an invasive hedge or trees crowding or overshadowing the plants is not desirable, some near-by windbreak on the north and east will act as a shelter from winter frosts. A position facing south or west with a gentle slope is ideal, so that the sun-loving plants may be set on the higher ground and those liking a moist soil, such as Mint or Angelica, can be placed in the lower, damper spots.

In a small garden, however, it is not easy to find the ideal spot; but a patch of sunny, open ground with a wall or fence as protection is the next best thing. And, if no other ground is available, it may be possible to find a few square yards in the vegetable garden or allotment. When only a corner of the garden can be spared, avoid dark chill patches under trees and that dull, rather dingy no-man's-land which unfortunately most of us possess at the end of the garden, for sunshine is essential if herbs are to produce their best.

A full day of sunshine, whenever possible, is all the more important if the garden soil happens to be of cold, heavy clay. The ideal plot for herbs is of medium light soil, thus ensuring good drainage and making digging and weeding not too laborious. But even with the heartbreaking clay soils, great improvements may be made by proper cultivation. The main point with such a soil is to get it dug in the autumn, and to let the winter frosts and snow break it down to a more friable condition for spring cultivation and planting.

CULTIVATION

During the winter months, many happy moments can be spent planning the herb-garden and selecting the plants; first those really necessary, and then letting your imagination run riot over the less familiar. Most herb catalogues are very helpful in defining the uses of the various kinds of herbs, and this may be some guide to the beginner in herbal knowledge. Still, selection, of course, must be a matter of individual taste, though a few hints may be of use.

Most nurserymen include in their general catalogues a variety of herb seeds and plants, while there are quite a few who specialise in a great variety of sweet and physick herbs, but starting from scratch in this way is going to be rather expensive. The fact that a large number of herbs can be grown from cuttings, root divisions and layers helps to solve this financial problem. Such plants as Rosemary, Thyme, Sage, Lavender, Mint, Balm, Hyssop, Marjoram and others may all be acquired in this way, either from old stocks or from friends' gardens.

Growing plants from seed is a slower method of producing a herb-garden, but it is quite satisfactory, except with Mint and Sage, which rarely come up to the expectation of the growing plants. A few annual herbs which must, of course, be raised from seed each year include Basil, Chervil, Coriander, Dill, Cumin, Aniseed, Marigold. Constant propagation by one method or another is to be recommended to keep a herb-garden planted satisfactorily.

As early as possible in the spring the ground should be dug over, and it is usually only necessary to fork in well-decayed compost or manure for such plants as Bergamot, Mint, Angelica, Liquorice and a few others. If possible, small amounts of seed may be sown in boxes or pots, as some are slow in germinating and are not easy to distinguish from the weed seedlings in the open ground. When weather and soil are favourable, the seedlings can be transplanted to their permanent positions.

If pots and boxes are not available, seed may be sown outdoors in rows in late spring, and thinned out as soon as the plants are large enough to stand the strain of being moved. If the weather is very dry, they will need watering, preferably in the evening from a fine-rosed watering-can. Gentle hoeing round the young plants keeps down weeds, leaves the soil loose, and, according to general belief, helps to retain moisture.

Just a few herbs are grown by separation of the bulbs, including Garlic, Chives, Star of Bethlehem, the Welsh or Everlasting Onion, and if the beds of these are turned over every year, so many bulbels will be collected that spare ones may be sold or passed to friends.

ARRANGEMENT

The lay-out of the herb-garden must again be according to personal taste, but certain points are worth remembering. For instance, it is a great pity to overcrowd the garden to begin with, as the occupants will soon spread, and, if there are any gaps, others may be put in from time to time. Another reason for careful spacing is that herbs will be required for the kitchen, and easy access to them is most desirable. To avoid too much treading, occasional small bricks or paving between the plants will be helpful, and trailing growths will soon make them not too evident.

Gardeners now are very divided as to the arrangement of

plants, some saying it is best to grow them according to height, so that tall-shooting herbs like Mullein, Foxglove, Comfrey and Sweet Cicely are placed at the back, while others prefer a more undulating effect, but in any case, low-growing herbs such as Thyme, Chamomile, Chives must be near the front of the border or they will not be seen. An obvious idea is to arrange those herb plants which are in constant demand – Mint, Sage, Parsley, Thyme and Marjoram – within easy reach.

In a large herb-garden this method need not apply, for plants of differing heights can be set in the various beds, and access to them will be easy by means of the paths. In the writer's own herb-garden medicinal and sweet herbs all grow delightfully together, but some gardeners may prefer to have what one might call a 'kitchen herb' garden entirely by itself. This really is not possible to achieve, as nearly all the kitchen or culinary herbs are also used in medicine. The common belief is that Caraway seed is grown entirely for confectionery, but as a matter of fact most of it is grown for drug purposes.

Also, I exclude from my garden all the poisonous herbs, for though there is a certain gloomy beauty in Henbane, Deadly Nightshade and Thornapple, too much danger is attached to the plants to make them at all companionable. Beside this, these narcotic plants are never required in the house, and if the plants are being grown commercially, these unpleasantly evil-smelling 'pain-killers' will have a plot to themselves.

Another point which can be settled only by the gardener is whether some stone ornament, such as an old sundial or bird-bath, with low-growing herbs, like Chamomile, filling the niches about the base, should be a feature of the herb-border or garden. Some people, too, like to dot their gardens with little stone animals or figures, though many of us recoil from this with distaste. And the interspersing of genuine herb-plants with brightly coloured but 'unherbal' flowers, such as Love in a Mist, Thrift, Honesty or Pinks, must be a matter of choice.

It was the fashion once to border herb-beds with Box, but this is a slow-growing plant, and apt to harbour slugs and other pests, though Box itself might have a place in the herb-garden, as it is one of the more useful medicinal plants. Knot gardening – the arrangement of plants in intricate interlacing patterns – often a feature of Tudor herb-gardens, is not to be advised, as it entails far too much work in keeping it neat.

A herb-garden may be of any size and shape to suit the

amount of ground that can be spared and the time the gardener can allow for its cultivation. It is as well to have plenty of walking space with the herbs set out in clumps in a bed of any shape that is fancied. Paths may be of crazy paving, bricks, or, most delightful, but entailing constant clipping, of Chamomile, Thyme or Burnet. Grass, provided it is kept well cut, is a lovely surround, but rammed earth or clinker paths are alternatives.

I have happy recollections of a herb-garden I once walked in with old rose red walls as background. In spring-time grew Primroses, sweet Violets, purple and pink and cream, and Cowslips; all quite legitimate, as they are useful drug plants. Against the walls clambered Sweet Briar, Damask and Cabbage Roses, white and yellow Jasmine, and the white Burnet Rose, useful both for medicine or perfumes. Foxgloves, Mullein and Comfrey, both white and purple, grew up beyond the roses, and at each corner of the garden was a gloriously green Bay Laurel. Herbs were grown in little beds with vivid grass between.

Once the herb-border or garden is established, it involves little trouble. If herbs are required for their leaves, flower heads must be cut as soon as they appear. After flowering, all dead straggly blooms should be rigorously cut away. Plants produced mainly for their flowers and seeds, such as Marigold, Borage, Caraway, Dill and Anise will scatter their seeds with rich prodigality for another year. Angelica and Parsley too are other self-sowers, which saves a good deal of work the following spring. And, of course, weeding and trimming are most important to avoid an untidy appearance. If all this is done, even in darkest winter your herb-garden will present a lovely sea of grey-green tints 'most heartening to the minde'.

PLAN OF A HERB BORDER

North Fence

FENNEL	WHITE HOREHOUND	TARRAGON		
BERGAMOT	DILL	CHERVIL		
PEPPERMINT	HYSSOP	TANSY		
PENNYROYAL	MINTS	SALAD BURNET		
CHIVES	THYME			

PATH

ANGELICA	BALM	SWEET CICELY	IRIS
ROSEMARY	CARAWAY	LAVENDER	BORAGE
RUE	MARIGOLD	SAVORY	
PARSLEY	MARJORAM	RED SAGE SAGE	CLARY
THYME	CHAMOMILE		

GARDEN PATH

South

West

East

199

BOOKS FOR FURTHER STUDY

A great number of books on herbs of wide and varied interest have been written. Among them are the following:

GRIEVE, M. (Mrs) *A Modern Herbal*. (Jonathan Cape, London.) (1932)

WHEELWRIGHT, E. G. *The Physick Garden*. (Jonathan Cape, London.) (1934)

ARBER, AGNES *Herbals, their Origin*. (1912)

LEYEL, C. F. (Mrs) *The Magic of Herbs*. (Jonathan Cape, London.) (1920)

HEWER, D. G. *Practical Herb Growing*. (G. Bell and Sons, Ltd., London.) (1942)

BROWN, C. R. and B. *Salads and Herbs*. (J. B. Lippincott Co., New York.) (1938)

GERARD'S *Herbal* (*Leaves from*). (John Lane, The Bodley Head, London.) (1931)

POTTER'S *Cyclopaedia of Botanical Drugs*. (Potter and Clarke, London.)

CULPEPER, *British Herbal*. (1653.)

KEEN and ARMSTRONG, *Herb Gathering*. (Brome and Schimmer, Ltd., London.) (1941)

TEETGEN, A. B. *Profitable Herb Growing*. (George Newnes, Ltd., London.) (1919)

ROHDE, E. S. *Herbs and Herb Gardening*. (The Medici Society, London.) (1936)

Ministry of Agriculture. Bulletin No. 125. *Culinary Herbs*. (1942)

Ministry of Agriculture. Bulletin No. 121. *Medicinal Herbs*. (1941)

INDEX

THE BUILDINGS OF ENGLAND

This series, edited and compiled by Nikolaus Pevsner, has been launched to meet a growing demand from students and travellers for more detailed information about the history and architecture of the buildings they visit. Its aim is to provide a complete and authoritative introduction to the churches, monuments, and large houses, in fact to every structure of interest in a county, from prehistoric remains to the latest building of note, treating them village by village and town by town, and in the case of churches describing not only the exterior but also the furnishings, such as pulpits, roof-bosses, and rood-screens. Each volume contains a long general introduction to the architectural history of the county, a map and a large section of illustrations. Volumes now available are:

'Inventories these books are, and wonderfully detailed ones. But they are much more than that. On every page one is continually made aware – sometimes by a sentence of comment, sometimes by as little as a single word, sometimes even by what isn't said – of learning, intelligence, and taste of work, placing, testing, and assessing. So far as architecture is concerned, this series will relegate most other guides to the status of picture books.' – *Architects Journal*

*Most of these volumes are available in
a bound edition at 7s 6d or 8s 6d*

THE PENGUIN HANDBOOKS

This is a series of practical manuals on gardening, farming, domestic affairs, and similar matters by acknowledged experts, all written primarily for the layman who starts without any knowledge at all. But they are of interest and value also to the professional, who wants some guidance on a particular question or another opinion on his subject. The same size as ordinary Penguins, they have decorative covers. The volumes at present available are:

KING PENGUINS

The King Penguins are handsomely illustrated books, each dealing with some aspect of the arts. They are slightly larger (7¼ by 4¾ in.) than the standard Penguins, and are bound in decorated boards. In every case the text is written by an authority on the subject, and the illustrations are tastefully chosen and carefully reproduced. King Penguins are the result of an unusual blending – sound scholarship, lively and perceptive editing, superb illustrating, and painstaking production. A few of the volumes available are:

ACKERMANN'S CAMBRIDGE – *R. Ross Williamson*

A selection of colour plates from Ackermann's *History of the University of Cambridge* (*1815*), with an introduction (K 59)   4s

ACKERMANN'S OXFORD – *H. M. Colvin*

This selection not only includes sixteen colour plates from Ackermann's *History of the University of Oxford*, but also eight black-and-white figures from his contemporary, James Ingram's *Memorials of Oxford* (K 69)   5s

EGYPTIAN PAINTINGS – *Nina M. Davies*

Sixteen colour plates show scenes and aspects of life in ancient Egypt. The plates belong to a large series made by the author for various authorities, including the Metropolitan Museum of New York (K 71)   5s

MOUNTAIN BIRDS – *R. A. H. Coombes*

With sixteen plates by G. E. Lodge and an essay by R. A. H. Coombes of the Zoology Department of the British Museum (K 67)
    4s 6d

MEDIEVAL CARVINGS IN EXETER CATHEDRAL
  – *C. J. P. Cave*

64 pages of photographs and an authoritative text describing the thirteenth- and fourteenth-century sculpture and decorations (K 62)
    4s 6d

SEMI-PRECIOUS STONES – *Nora Wooster*

Sixteen colour plates by Arthur Smith and an essay by Mrs Wooster of the Brooklyn Chrystallographic Laboratory, Cambridge (K 65)
    4s 6d

BOOKS ON PLANTS
In various series

A Book of Mosses – Paul W. Richards
A concise and up-to-date account with sixteen colour plates reproduced from Johannes Hedwig's work, first published in Germany, 1787–97 (κ57) 3s

Common Wild Flowers – John Hutchinson
Over 200 British wild flowers described, and illustrated (A153) 2s

Flowers of the Meadow – Geoffrey Grigson
Twenty-four colour plates by Robin Tanner and a long essay by Geoffrey Grigson, well known as a poet and naturalist (κ53)
3s

More Common Wild Flowers – John Hutchinson
A sequel to *Common Wild Flowers* (see above) which illustrates and describes over 200 more British wild flowers (A180) 2s

Poisonous Fungi – J. Ramsbottom
Full descriptions and methods of identifying the dangerous fungi, and sixteen colour plates (κ23) 2s 6d

See How They Grow – Mary Field, J. V. Durden, F. Smith
A glance at the wonders and beauties of botany through the medium of the film (A242) 3s 6d

Trees in Britain – S. R. Badmin
Thirty trees and the uses of their woods are described. Pictures of each tree show it in summer and winter (PP31) 2s

Tulipomania – Wilfrid Blunt
An attractive study of a 17th-century botanical cult, with sixteen colour plates from newly-discovered originals by Alexander Marshal (κ44) 3s

Wild Flowers of the Chalk – John Gilmour
Text by John Gilmour, ex-Director of the Royal Horticultural Society's Gardens, and plates by Irene Hawkins (κ37) 2s 6d